Louis Pasteur

Louis Pasteur

The Man and
his Theories

HILAIRE CUNY
translated by
PATRICK EVANS

THE SCIENTIFIC BOOK CLUB
121 CHARING CROSS ROAD
LONDON W.C.2.

Edited by Jacques Ahrweiler

First British edition published 1965 by Souvenir Press Ltd.
34 Bloomsbury Street, London W.C.1.
and simultaneously in Canada
by The Ryerson Press, Toronto 2, Canada

*Printed in Great Britain by
The Camelot Press Ltd., London and Southampton*

Contents

SELECTED WRITINGS

THÈSES

DE

PHYSIQUE ET DE CHIMIE,

présentées

À LA FACULTÉ DES SCIENCES DE PARIS,

LE   AOUT 1847,

Par M. L. PASTEUR,

Ancien élève de l'École Normale, agrégé préparateur de Chimie à cette École

———•——◦◦◦——•———

PARIS,

IMPRIMERIE DE BACHELIER,

Rue du Jardinet, 12.

1847.

I

What Manner of Man was He?*

THE GENIUS AND THE MAN

LOUIS PASTEUR was born at Dôle, in the Jura, on December 27, 1822. Twenty years later, in 1842, he entered the École Normale. After another twenty years, in 1862, he was elected a member of the Académie des Sciences. And after a further twenty years, in 1882, he was elected to the Académie Française. In the meantime innumerable prizes, decorations and academic titles had been conferred on him. Despite not being a doctor, he had been made a member of the Académie de Médecine and had revolutionized standard medical practice. His social origins were of the humblest. From the age of forty-six onwards he was an invalid, but his brilliant genius had triumphed over all the dangers which ignorance, envy, illness, his own intransigence and even fame—that most treacherous of pitfalls—had placed in his path.

Today Pasteur is known everywhere, not only among specialists and learned people generally, but among the public at large; and this, after all, is the ultimate accolade. I have seen a portrait or bust of him displayed in laboratories the world over, in Moscow, Paris, London, Sofia, Budapest, Berlin, Prague, Algiers. . . . There are over a hundred medical institutes and international scientific centres bearing his name, and there can

* At the end of the book will be found a Glossary of technical terms which might cause difficulty to the layman.

be but few men and women alive who have not heard that name uttered at least once. And everyone is indebted to Pasteur, more or less directly, for the successful treatment of some ailment or other.

The layman, however, usually associates the name of Pasteur with the struggle against rabies. But antirabic inoculation was merely a spectacular by-product of discoveries whose importance is much wider, and whose roots lay in a major human preoccupation: the search for the secret of life. This aspect of Pasteur's activities has often been overlooked, even by the well-informed, and I have had the privilege of interesting more than one foreign biologist by telling him of the curious experiments carried out by Pasteur at Strasbourg, Lille and Arbois in an attempt to show that molecular dissymmetry (which is one of the hall-marks of organic matter) had as its fundamental cause a cosmic factor which was itself dissymmetrical.

This quest for the origin of molecular dissymmetry, which he hoped would lead to a partial solution of the mystery of life, was something Pasteur could never quite bring himself to abandon. We shall see him laying it on one side at the instigation of Biot (who regarded it as a merely metaphysical preoccupation), at the time when the glory of his early reputation was about to burst upon him; but we shall also see him resuming it when the War of 1870-1 forced him to retreat to his old family home, far from his laboratories in Paris, free from academic pressures and other cares and obligations and, above all, free from the need to convert his discoveries into practical applications.

It will be recalled that one of the major conflicts Pasteur had to sustain, one which extended over a considerable portion of his career, was his fight against the active partisans of heterogenesis and, in a more general sense, against the almost officially established doctrine that, in certain forms and under certain conditions, spontaneous generation was a real possibility. His experiments had taught him, on the contrary, that spontaneous generation was absolutely impossible *in present circumstances*; that is to say, at the present stage of the evolution of life on earth. Darwin himself had expressed the same thought when he wrote:

"If we imagine that in some warm little pool, containing all sorts of ammoniacal salts and phosphates, a proteinic compound has been formed by chemical means with the help of light, heat and electricity; this compound, ready to undergo more complex changes, would today be immediately devoured and absorbed."

Publicly, however, at the Sorbonne, Pasteur declared: "Spontaneous generation is something I have looked for without finding it, but I do not believe it to be impossible." By this he meant that he believed inorganic matter to possess the property of self-organisation; for he had arrived at the opinion, the conviction almost, that the constituents of lifeless or supposedly lifeless matter were identical with those of living matter. To this extent at least it is safe to say that he was in perfect agreement with Darwin and the materialists.

But it would be disingenuous to portray Pasteur as a materialist. He had nothing whatsoever in common with the materialists of his own time, whose banal, over-simplified ideas were castigated in a lapidary sentence of Pavlov's: "I condemn myopic materialism which, in a gross, premature fashion, simplifies the object and debases it in the eyes of every clearsighted, vital observer." Many of Pasteur's statements show him to have been close to the scientific or dialectical materialism of our own day; the same can be said of Teilhard de Chardin—who, like Pasteur, believed that spiritual things were real.

Pasteur's thinking was subtle and finely shaded. Here is a remark of his which everyone would do well to ponder: "You say that matter is antecedent to life and has existed from all eternity. How can you be sure that the unceasing march of science will not one day . . . force us to conclude that life, not matter, has existed from all eternity? . . . If you wish to be ranked among the *scientific* minds—the only minds which count —you must get rid of *a priori* notions and arguments and confine yourselves to rigorous inference from observed fact; you must have nothing more to do with inference from mere hypotheses."

This statement has always been interpreted as a defence of idealism against materialism. But what new look does it acquire in the light of our present-day knowledge? It is a fact, established experimentally, that matter consists of concentrations of energy—the energy of the universe, an energy about which we know nothing save that it possesses extraordinary powers of self-organisation or (if you prefer to put it this way) of physico-chemical complication and, beyond that, of biological elaboration. As for thought, or psychological activity—and in saying this we are not trying to claim that human thinking is merely a complex of conditioned reflexes—it makes its appearance in this framework as a new quality, born of a countless host of interactions between the external and internal environment. Where, in all this, are we to lay down the boundaries of what we call "life" and "matter"?

We must insist that, while we have no intention of trying to portray Pasteur as a crypto-rationalist, he was worlds away from the anthropomorphic attitude of the religious party, with their belief in a myth of a Creation—the party which, as we shall see, tried at one stage to claim him as their own. As we watch him pondering on the Infinite, and the "mysterious hidden power in things", we cannot but ask whether he was not a good deal closer to the philosophy of Spinoza than his biographers have usually conceded. He does not say, with a thinker of a later generation, Lucien Cuénot: "Pantheism is simple, it has no theology . . . scientists are its priests, research is its prayer, and its temples are everywhere." But he does earnestly exhort his disciples, "Pay all due concern, I beg of you, to those sacred edifices which are known, so expressively, as *laboratories*. Demand that they be as numerous and as fine as possible; for they are the temples of the future. . . . It is in them that men grow to full stature and become better beings; in them, that men learn to decipher the works of nature, works of universal progress and harmony, whereas men's own works are all too often at once the fruit and the cause of barbarism, fanaticism and destruction."

Einstein said: "The man who is not familiar with the sense of mystery and has lost his capacity for astonishment, for over-whelming reverence, is as good as dead."

Pasteur never lost that capacity. His career was a succession of controversies; his private life was not without vicissitudes; he was rigid in his adherence to fundamental scientific principles; and, in his later days, the public showered adulation on him as "the conqueror of hydrophobia". But through it all he kept the gift of boyish wonder which is common to all true scientists —that is, all scientists who realise that man's knowledge, how-ever great it may become, is only a tiny fraction of the infinite mystery of the universe.

A GREAT WORKER

All we are attempting to do in this book is to trace the main out-lines of Pasteur's scientific activities. The immediately obvious point about him is his unusual capacity for work. At times we even feel that he dissipated his energies by spreading them too far afield in biology and physiology, after starting in physics and chemistry. But this impression is misleading. Doubtless, when he set out on his dazzling epic of discovery, Pasteur had no clear idea in what direction it was to take him. He chose the study of crystals on grounds at once aesthetic and personal. It is almost true to say that his youthful love of drawing determined the direction of his scientific endeavours. He was attracted in the first place by the beauty of crystalline structures, and it was his affection for his teachers, Delafosse and Laurent, which made him choose a *Study of Phenomena Connected with the Rotatory Polarisation of Liquids* as the title of his physics thesis. But once he had succeeded in showing that dissymmetry was the fundamental characteristic of organic structures and of the substances pro-duced by living organisms, he advanced firmly into bio-chemistry.

At that stage it was impossible for Pasteur to know where he was going: he had to clear the ground ahead of himself as he went. He travelled Europe in search of paratartrate, and made his way into places where the presence of a scientist was least to be expected—wine-cellars, warehouses, vineyards, breweries, stock-breeding establishments; and in these places he carried out his experiments, gave demonstrations, and delivered speeches which were the follow-up to the challenges he issued with such unusual boldness to his contradictors. No scientist had behaved like this before, and no one has done it since. What he was in fact doing was to seize every chance of acquiring new knowledge and building up the new branch of science which was entirely his own creation, and which he called "*la microbie*"; in present-day parlance, micro-biology.

If we glance at his work in chronological sequence we find it to be admirably consistent: crystallography, molecular dissymmetry, the fundamentals of stereochemistry, fermentation, anaerobiosis, proof of the impossibility of spontaneous generation—from which it followed that the whole realm of microbiology existed and awaited investigation—and, finally, the struggle against pathogenic bacteria, with its natural corollaries: asepsis, inoculation, the beginnings of serum therapy and immunisation.

The various practical applications of Pasteur's discoveries, such as pasteurisation, were merely episodes in his rapid ascent to the highest altitudes of scientific discovery. The therapeutic methods developed either by him, or by his followers in his lifetime and after his death (and still being developed today, when the traditions of the Pasteur Institute are as flourishing as ever), bear witness to the vitality and fruitfulness of the tree of life which he succeeded in planting for mankind's benefit.

Many of even the most modern techniques are derived from hypotheses which he was the first to formulate but which he had neither the time nor the means to submit to the test of experiment. Fleming said: "Without Pasteur I would have been nothing." Pasteur, in fact, had prophetically foreseen the possibility of turning microbial antagonisms to practical account. He wrote: "Among the lowliest organisms, even more than in the larger animal and vegetable species" [here he was referring to the Darwinian theory of the "struggle for existence" and that of "natural selection", which is a possible consequence from it], "life preys on life; and this antagonism perhaps gives us grounds for expecting great discoveries in the therapeutic field."

In 1888 one of his colleagues at Lyons, Professor Gabriel Roux (not to be confused with his namesake, famous for discovering the treatment for diphtheria), and, subsequently, a pupil of Roux, Ernest Duchesne, conducted researches with this aim in view. Their investigations showed that guinea-pigs infected with Eberth's bacillus (the organism responsible for typhoid fever) were slower to succumb if they were given injections of a preparation of *Penicillium glaucum*, a mould very closely related to that from which Fleming was to extract penicillin.

Pasteur did not believe in the watertight division of science into "pure" and "applied". In his view, there was fundamental research; and there were "the applications of science", which, as he used to say himself, were a very different matter. Pure science was his lifelong passion. But he did not let this make him look down on applied science, whose activities were capable of improving man's lot, curing disease and hence, like theoretical science itself, of contributing towards the advance of knowledge.

Moreover, he was given to understand—as if he needed telling!—that the subsidies so stingily handed out to him must serve some practical purpose. A certain M. de Cardaillac, with all the lofty pride of a senior bureaucrat (he was the permanent head of the Ministry of Public Buildings), even went so far as to say, "Your fermentations are costing us a lot of money, sir, but we are expecting magnificent results"!

PASTEUR AND THE PRACTICAL SIDE OF LIFE

So great is the disproportion between the poverty of French laboratories in the second half of the nineteenth century and the present-day shortage of funds for scientific research that no comparison can be drawn between the two. (And this remains true even if we disregard the grossly inflated subsidies now being lavished on research of military importance.) There is a well-known portrait of Pasteur having to kneel in order to work in his little room at the École Normale. His colleagues were no better off: Claude Bernard was working in a cellar at the

Collège de France, and Wurtz had to make do with a grubby attic at the Musée Dupuytren.

There is no denying that Pasteur was a careerist, and that while he laboured for the advancement of science he was equally eager to advance himself. M. Ernest Kahane says unequivocally: "On occasion he would enlist his teachers and friends—Biot, Dumas, his father-in-law Laurent, Sénarmont, and others—in support of some move which would promote his university career." Professor René Dubos adds that Pasteur, as "a Frenchman of the lower middle classes, coming from a family of restricted means, undoubtedly aspired after financial security".

His father was poor and had to struggle, or had had to do so in the early stages, to prevent his small business in hides and skins from collapsing; the son had naturally been taught not to despise money. Can any of us blame the father for that? Even today we have still not learnt what havoc is wreaked in society by money—which was invented as a means of exchange, but which has become a species of merchandise in itself, and the object of savage competition.

There are many cases in which the speech and actions of Pasteur show him to have been completely disinterested. We have noted that he never neglected the practical side of his discoveries, since he thought, rightly, that in this way he could help mankind. But he made it quite clear that this was not the primary aim of his life and that he was not interested in practical applications for the sake of his pocket. He went to some pains in explaining this to General Favé, Napoleon III's aide-de-camp, presumably after some ill-considered remark by that officer or one of the courtiers in his immediate circle:

"Any scientist who allows himself to be lured by the prospect of industrial applications automatically ceases to be the servant of pure science; he clutters up his life and thinking with pre-occupations which paralyse his faculty for discovery. I am sure that if I had involved myself in the industrial side of my work on vinegar production, I would still be involved in it now; and if I launched out into the industrial exploitation of my present research on wine, I would be embroiled in it for a long time to come. . . . A large number of others are trying out the procedures arising out of my work in connection with wine; for my own part, I watch these efforts with the curiosity of a scientist. But my mind remains at liberty, and the diseases of silkworms are at present arousing the same ardour in me as, two years ago, you saw me showing when I was embarking on the study of wine."

Pasteur's correspondence, certainly, is full of approaches of a financial order to various ministries; but almost none of these requests was aimed at his own personal benefit. Most of them were for credits for equipping a laboratory, or the supply of materials or experimental animals. Most of the money he received in the form of scientific prizes was used up in this way, but, of course, it was not enough. And Mme. Pasteur, very rightly keeping her eye on the security of her children and the family as a whole, often begged him to be more hard-headed.

An echo of these disagreements about money has come down to us in a letter in which Pasteur reveals that there has been a family argument about the possibility of exploiting the patents taken out for the methods he had developed for the better preservation of beer, wine and vinegar. The letter is addressed to General Favé, and ends with the observation that, in France, too much is expected from the State and too little from the individual citizen: "It is my opinion", Pasteur says, "that disinterested scientific thinking ought to be encouraged, because it is one of the prime sources of that progress in pure research without which there can be no progress in the application of science to practical production." And he allows himself to be overridden, and to accept some degree of profit from the exploitation of his patents abroad, only because (as he explains) "my wife, always thoughtful for our children's future, has given me seemingly unanswerable grounds for relaxing my scruples".

No such scruples had been felt by Liebig, a great biologist of the same period, who let his name be used in a shameless advertising campaign. The discredit thrown on scientific circles by this laxity was the reason why Pasteur, in 1882, declined an

offer from a Dutch financier for exclusive rights in the exploitation of his vaccines against anthrax and swine erysipelas in
certain foreign countries.

Pasteur and his collaborators did later share among themselves the profits from these patents outside France. But the
royalties on pasteurisation were turned over to the State; and
those on the use of Pasteur's vaccines in France were allocated
to the Institut Pasteur, not to Pasteur himself.

His unselfish attitude is further shown by the fact that he
never accepted fees for honorary posts; he let himself be paid
only for work in appointments where he was actively responsible for the outcome. In his view, eminent men were guilty of
dishonesty if they adopted the current practice of collecting as
many lucrative posts as possible, thus blighting the prospects of
subordinates who did the real work and should have reaped
the benefit.

Pasteur made so little money out of science that Metchnikoff
recalls: "When his health became too bad for him to get about
on foot, as he usually did, and he had to hire a horse and
carriage by the year, the question assumed momentous proportions; only after much thought and arithmetic was the decision
finally taken. In a future age, when the social importance of
science is generally recognised, it will seem incredible that a
man like Pasteur, who had brought innumerable benefits to the
human race, should have worried at the height of his fame
about the cost of local transport."

If Pasteur was personally subsidised from the Imperial privy
purse (and it seems likely that he was), it happened only now
and again and on a very small scale; and it was certainly not
the reason for his regarding the régime with a favourable eye—
so favourable, indeed, that his relations with Napoleon III and
the Imperial court are a chapter in his life-story which makes
painful reading.

PASTEUR AND POLITICS

It is almost impossible to outline Pasteur's political views—for
the simple reason that he had none. In his profession of faith to

the electorate of Arbois, when he was trying for a seat in the Senate of the newly-created Third Republic, he admitted as much with complete candour. His political inexperience was such that he simply said what he thought!

"Science, in our century, is the soul of a nation's prosperity and the wellspring of progress of all kinds. Politics, with its endless, weary disputations, may seem to be our guide—but what an illusion! Our real guidance comes from a few scientific discoveries and their practical utilisation. . . . What I shall be representing in the Senate is science."

Such ingenuous honesty, such a lack of the tricks of the hustings, of course aroused no approval in the electors, who were a crowd of miniature politicians themselves. He was defeated; and took his defeat well.

Having established this much, we have to admit that almost throughout his lifetime Pasteur was a conservative of the most unenlightened kind. It may be surprising that so bright an intelligence should not have chosen better, or simply abstained from making a choice at all. But we have to remember the contemporary context, the extraordinary vitality of the age, the influence of his friends and background, and the pressure of expediency. Yet some men successfully resisted the dangers. We are therefore forced to admit that Pasteur was essentially a conformist with an opportunistic streak: a disappointing thing in so great a scientist, especially one who by nature was pitiless towards the errors of others. The painful impression comes to us that his ambitions sometimes got the better of his innate generosity; and that his patriotism, on occasion, degenerated into chauvinism.

Thus, for example, during the Franco-Prussian War (1870-1), we see Pasteur automatically condemning the German nation as a whole, without distinction, and, moreover, without taking into account the mistakes of Napoleon III and his ministers and general staff. It is distressing to read, from the pen of a benefactor of humanity, the sort of thing which was later to be perpetrated by a cheap patriotic poet like Paul Déroulède—paeans of praise for the heroism of a soldier's death, uttered at a safe distance from the battlefield. Pasteur writing, "O, happy dead!" and, even more outrageously:

"I want to see France resisting to the last man and the last defence-work. I want to see the war prolonged into the depths of winter, so that, with the elements rallying to our side, all those vandals confronting us shall perish of cold and hunger and disease. All my work, to my dying day, will bear as an inscription, 'Hatred towards Prussia! Revenge! Revenge!'" —no, this Pasteur is not Pasteur.

But what about the courtier complacently depicting the splendours of the Imperial Court? Was that Pasteur either?

PASTEUR AND THE GOLDEN CALF OF AUTHORITY

Pasteur had been invited by Napoleon to the Château de Compiègne, the most fashionable and worldly of the Imperial residences. One might have expected him to be shocked by the contrast between such luxury and the poverty of the people. That poverty may not have been exactly as depicted, luridly, by Eugène Sue in *Les Mystères de Paris*, or Victor Hugo in *Les Misérables*; still, it was not so very different. And yet we find Pasteur, on Friday, December 1, 1865, dazzled by the spectacle which he describes in a letter to his wife:

"At half-past eleven we went into the drawing-room. The ladies and gentlemen who were to follow the hunt on horseback were wearing hunting clothes [*sic*]. The Emperor and Empress, arm in arm, came out of their private apartments and entered the drawing-room. Everyone drew aside; their Majesties, with a greeting for everybody as they passed, made their way into the dining-room. The company followed. Luncheon. Directly after it we went out into the garden, where carriages were waiting. We entered the carriages and set off, escorted by out-riders. [A description of the hunt follows.] We came back and dressed. At seven o'clock we went down to the drawing-room. The Emperor, giving his arm to the Empress, traversed the room, with salutations such as I described above. Everyone followed. On reaching the end of the table, the Emperor left the Empress and they went to their separate places and sat down, the rest of us sitting wherever we wished. The ambassadors and their wives, and the duchesses, were placed to the right and left of their Majesties. At luncheon the Emperor had the wife of the Prefect of the Oise, Mme. Chevreau, on his left. The same ceremony took place at the end of dinner. We all re-entered the drawing-room and split up into groups. I was introduced to Mme. la Marquise de Lagrange by the Empress's Chamberlain, and chatted with her for some time. Then Admiral Jurien de la Gravière introduced me to Mme. Lagrenée . . . the very lady who had been sitting at the Empress's right hand yesterday, when I was invited to join the group which included Her Majesty."

From letter to letter, the description of this flummery goes on, without a trace of irony. With fatuous seriousness Pasteur communicates every detail of what he has seen. On the Sunday morning he writes:

"We went into a charming room, something between a study and a drawing-room. The Empress, in a charming red woollen gown (a kind of *peignoir*, neither a habit, a formal dress nor a *sac*), and with her hair uncovered, came in and greeted us and went across to a little table on which the lamp was standing. . . ."

Nowhere can one find an intelligent observation on the emptiness of these festivities, in which he obviously feels a strange fascination. He becomes positively lyrical in describing the "good humour" of "Their Majesties". He even retails the latest tattle. He names Lord Dudley, "about whom people are saying all sorts of things and who, it seems, has really been out of his mind". Pasteur adds that this grandee has just married a ravishingly pretty girl of nineteen: "I just don't know how to describe how beautifully dressed this young lady was. Mme. de Lagrenée assures me that her necklace—five rows of pearls, truly magnificent—cost 700,000 francs."

Unfortunately, there is worse to follow. It is hard to understand how he came to write the letter given below, the closing passage of which is closely connected with the assassination of the journalist Victor Noir by another nephew of Napoleon I,

Pierre Bonaparte, who was acquitted, whereas Rochefort, who had been bravely attempting to arouse public opinion (the result of his campaign being public disturbances), was sentenced to six months in prison.

Here is the letter:

"My dear Marshal,—I hasten to thank you for your letter, which made me blush with confusion when I learnt from it that it had been in the Empress's hands and that the Emperor had been informed of its contents. I, less than any other man, deserve commendation for my devotion to Their Majesties. I have benefited by their kindness more than once, and especially when I had just been attacked by an illness which put my life in danger. My wife and children were in great need of consolation and support at that juncture.

"My father brought me up always to admire the great man [i.e. Napoleon I] and to hate the Bourbons. He was conscripted in 1811 and, as a non-commissioned officer in a line regiment, fought at Arcis-sur-Aube, where he was decorated. To him, the Emperor was a superhuman being. After the Imperial departure from Fontainebleau his loyalty brought a series of persecutions on his head, although he was only a tanner in a small way of business at Dôle; there were a great many legitimists there. You should have heard him, the day before the ballot for the election of the president of the Republic, laughing at the hopes of the supporters of Cavaignac. He said to them, 'Haven't you ever read Béranger's *Souvenirs du Peuple*? Have you never been inside the cottage of the poorest peasant in the poorest village in France? Have you ever found a cottage in which there wasn't a portrait of the great leader? They'll flock to the polls in battalions to vote for his nephew.' And he was right. I naturally inherited these feelings, which are part of the indispensable foundations of the power of the present dynasty. It was those same feelings which inspired the immortal campaign of 1814 and brought a chorus of applause from all France at the time of the return from Elba.

"A ruling house which has these memories to draw upon, memories of glory and greatness, and which is, moreover, strengthened by such a reign as that now unrolling before our eyes, is unshakeable. It is a fine thing to walk abroad without an escort, in a city of two million souls still vibrating with terror and indignation at the outrages of impotent maniacs. Courage such as this is fit to fill a nation with exalted pride, especially a nation like ours, which, in all Europe, is the one which most loves to feel that it is being ruled by an outstanding personality. But such bravery and trustfulness must not be carried to the pitch of temerity. I would wish the prefect of police to say to himself every morning, 'Henri IV was killed by the fanatic Ravaillac; and republican fanaticism is just as unscrupulous as religious fanaticism. . . .' "

PASTEUR AND DEMOCRACY

Pasteur, however, had not always been so outspoken an opponent of the republican idea. During the revolution of 1848 he enrolled in the Garde Nationale, subsequently writing to his father:

"I should be sorry to leave Paris just now. The scenes unrolling under our eyes contain beautiful, sublime lessons. And my fighting spirit mounts at the sounds of fighting and rioting, and, if necessary, I would fight with the greatest courage for the sacred cause of the Republic."

And in fact he offered his savings on "the altar of our native land". His father strongly advised him to make his gesture publicly known by inserting an announcement in a newspaper: "A gift to the country: 150 francs from the son of an old soldier decorated by the Emperor."

But this blaze of republican ardour soon burnt itself out; Pasteur settled down:

"Superficial minds, or those blinded by political passion [he wrote in the poster which he used during the Senatorial elections at Lons-le-Saunier, in 1876], worship the republican ideal enshrined in the great things accomplished by the Convention and the Comité de Salut Public. History shows such convictions to be totally erroneous. The salvation of France has been encompassed by her superiority in the sciences, and nothing else."

And, though he never attempted to defend the memory of Napoleon III, he accepted the Third Republic only with the greatest reservations. He was prepared to put up with it, provided it remained the republic of the conservative MacMahon, to whom he sent a message of good wishes. He regarded the Commune as "the Saturnalia of Paris"; and he wrote to the Emperor of Brazil that his reign offered "matter for contemplation to a citizen of a young republic which is having great difficulty in showing that its conceptions can bear fruit".

Pasteur was undoubtedly a technocrat. But without his knowing it—because he had failed to realise that certain excesses or errors of the revolutions in France during the eighteenth and nineteenth centuries were due to the fact that the people had been deliberately kept in a state of ignorance, and had not and could not have any revolutionary education and, in consequence, often reacted primitively—he had a tendency to accept government by dubious aristocratic cliques.

When Pasteur writes, "The only true democracy is that which makes it possible for every individual to contribute his maximum effort to the general life", he is giving us an excellent definition of the ideal cherished by all intelligent progressives in their desire for a better world, a world in which everyone, working in accordance with his means (it being agreed that every individual will have access to the highest culture, and will therefore become aware of his full duty as a member of the human race), will also receive in accordance with his needs. But Pasteur lapses into commonplace when he writes:

"Why is it that, alongside this fertile, vital democracy, there should exist another democratic spirit, which is barren and dangerous and which, on the pretext of I know not what chimerical ideal of equality, dreams of the State's absorbing, and even destroying, the individual? The flavour of this false democracy, I make bold to say, is the flavour of mediocrity. . . . This kind of democracy can be defined as the coalition of all who want to live without working, to consume without producing, to hold appointments without having trained for them, and to receive honours without deserving them. . . ."

This is a common error, and Pasteur falls into it because his judgement is superficial. There is no doubt of his sincerity; too many political adventurers convince, or have in the past convinced, ignorant crowds that by merely overthrowing the established order or by insistently pressing their claims they will inevitably achieve a higher standard of living—whereas, on the contrary, the only possible aim is to draw up a constructive social plan whose realisation will demand hard work from everybody, at least in the early stages, which will last several generations. Pasteur did not understand that the only champions of the brand of democracy he so rightly condemned were shameless and ambitious demagogues: just as, today, our plutocrats champion another brand of democracy, in which the permutations and combinations of professional politicians are such that the right of the people as a whole to choose its own representatives is illusory, not real. Democracy in which real governmental power is held by the people cannot possibly exist without an equally real cultural equality; and ignorance was still so widespread in the second half of the nineteenth century that Pasteur, who in any case was too busy to examine the problem fundamentally, was not altogether wrong in his repugnance towards a form of government which, on two previous occasions, had demonstrated its inadequacy. He can be reproached only for not having added (as he did in the case of the biological theory of spontaneous generation) a limiting clause: "*in the present circumstances . . .*".

In short, Pasteur as a scientist was a great revolutionary; but Pasteur the man accepted wholesale the narrow standards acquired from his upbringing.

2

His Background and Early Career

PASTEUR's father had been a non-commissioned officer in the armies of Napoleon I. He had received the decoration of the Legion of Honour from the Emperor in person. His nostalgia for those days was the source of the exacerbated patriotism, and the militarism, which were passed on to his children. But he was not the half-pay soldier of tradition, nursing his rancour in idleness and awaiting the return of the prisoner of St. Helena. Though his hopes revived at the time of the Hundred Days, he does not seem to have made that a pretext for abandoning the trade of leather-worker, which he had bravely resumed on quitting military service. At the time of Louis Pasteur's birth he owned and managed a small tannery which yielded a modest competence for his family and himself.

Pasteur's correspondence makes it easy to imagine the family atmosphere in the little house at Arbois, and Pasteur's son-in-law, M. René Vallery-Radot, has left a faithful description of it. The keynote was austerity. The conventionally approved sentiments were held in honour—affectionate esteem between members of the community, religion, and respect for the law. "Jean-Joseph Pasteur", writes Vallery-Radot, "was not a man who made friends easily. He never went into a café. On Sundays, in his overcoat brushed with military smartness, its broad lapel displaying the ribbon of the Legion of Honour—the style of ribbon worn in those days was visible at forty yards—he invariably went out walking on the road which connects Arbois with Besançon." The only regular visitors he allowed to his house were those whose "elevation of mind and heart entitled them to respect and friendship". These were a former Army doctor, Dumont; a provincial historian-cum-philosopher, Bousson, "a plump little man cast in a Benedictine mould, who was composing a work on the character of the inhabitants of Franche-Comté in general and Arbois in particular"; the Head-master of the local secondary school, M. Romanet, "whose daily concern was to raise the minds and hearts of his pupils to a yet loftier plane"; and Captain Barbier, an officer of the Parisian Garde Municipale, who used to spend his leave at Arbois.

It was at Barbier's instigation that Louis Pasteur made his first attempt to settle in Paris for his education. This was a complete failure. The boy was so homesick that he fell ill, and his father had to make the long, difficult journey from Arbois by stage-coach to bring him back. Louis then set about learning to draw, flinging himself into his work with something like frenzy; in his desire to make progress, he was willing to forgo the comforts of home life, and, since both his father and he felt that a return to Paris was "too daunting", it was decided that he should attend a boarding-school in Besançon.

Pasteur was never a distinguished pupil there. He was just a hard worker, a conscientious boy who stood out from his contemporaries only by his conspicuous talent for draughts-manship—but, as he wrote to his parents, "That won't take me to the École Normale. I'd rather come top of the class than get hundreds of commendations which don't amount to anything much." However, his conduct was so good that he was offered a job as a junior master; a tangible illustration, it must have seemed, of his father's principle that society always rewarded merit. And we find young Louis exhorting his sisters in this strain:

"Once again I urge you to work hard and love one another. An individual who gets used to hard work can thereafter never live without it. And work is the foundation of everything in this world. Knowledge raises us high above our fellows. Work depends on determination; moreover, it nearly always leads to success. In these three things, work, determination and success, lies the sum of human life; determination opens the door to a brilliant and prosperous career, hard work carries one over the threshold, and in the end comes the crown of success."

This is at once a caricature of Pasteur's own life and a true picture of many a brilliant career. Fortunately, Pasteur accomplished something which might well never have brought him the crown of worldly success. How many examples, from Galileo to Lamarck, show us that great minds can perfectly well do without that!

CONFLICTS OF IDEAS

Although he was simple in his ways, and one whose kindness to others gleamed out dazzlingly from time to time, Pasteur was never modest. And this is one of the signs of his honesty. In the position he came to occupy in adult life any modesty would have been false modesty. He was completely straightforward. Some of his values may have been narrow or even quite mistaken, but at least he never lied, to others or himself; and there is no reason for assuming that this strict integrity was easy to maintain.

Just after going to Besançon he wrote to his father:

"I still have the little book by M. Droz, which he was kind enough to lend me. I have never read anything more replete with wisdom, morality and virtue. I have one other of his works. They could not be more beautifully written; they have an irresistible charm which fills the soul, setting it ablaze with the sublimest, most generous feelings. In saying this I am not exaggerating in the least. On Sundays, when hearing Mass, I read nothing but the works of M. Droz, and whatever might be the views of religious bigotry about my doing so, I for my part believe that I am acting in conformity with all that is fine and real in religion."

At school in Besançon he had the chance of observing just

how twisted the mentality of some representatives of the Church could be, and he had good reason to prefer the secular counsels of the worthy M. Droz which, though somewhat simple in outlook, undoubtedly breathed an earnest moral spirit. It was probably his memories of this period which, when he had become a professor at the École Normale, led him to take his pupils' side in an application to the Minister of Education, Victor Duruy; students were compelled to attend Mass, and Pasteur, in his report to the Minister, requested that the officiating priest be invited to confine himself to the ritual and refrain from preaching, "since the sermons of the reverend almoner are frequently the reverse of impressive".

The pertinent episode in his Besançon period was described as follows in a letter home:

"My dear parents,—Here is a piece of news which is still a secret but which, as soon as it becomes known, will cause a terrific scandal. Our almoner is shortly to be expelled. His true character has long been known to every boarder, but had not so far leaked out in the town. His talent as a preacher and, even more, his hypocrisy, had caused him to be received by the best families in Besançon. He was riddled with debts and his behaviour inside the school was infamous, but his cloth prevented the truth from being known. You will perhaps ask me to specify his crimes—for that is what they must be called; but unfortunately they are the sort of thing one can't talk about. You will doubtless hear about them later, since the thing is bound to make a stir. I have always felt sure that before I finished my time here I should see that man expelled in disgrace. It is unfortunate, highly so, indeed, that religion should count such men among its ministers, and perhaps even more unfortunate that he should have been in charge of a school for ten years. Keep the matter secret; parts of it are still obscure. You can be quite sure that I shan't let anything out myself. You will hear it said that his gift for preaching has made him decide to become a missionary. . . ."

Pasteur indulged in one other gesture of revolt—a very brief one—against the established order. He was trying to make up his mind whether to enter the École Normale or the École Polytechnique:

"To my way of thinking, the careers made available via the Polytechnique are superior to teaching, with the exception of the military side. You know how much I hate all that—so much so that, if I did go to the Polytechnique, I would do everything in my power not to find myself in the artillery at the end of it."

This was the only time he spoke out against militarism. Indeed, we hear him striking a bellicose note in a letter to his father:

"You've read about the damaging blow we've just dealt to the Russian fleet. People are saying that Admiral Napier, who is in the Baltic, is planning to destroy Kronstadt; and it seems that, if he does, St. Petersburg can be reached without resistance in another couple of days."

He had an incomprehensible admiration for the man whom Victor Hugo, writing at the same time, was calling "Napoleon the Little". He waxed cheaply lyrical:

"You must be delighted with the Emperor, he has carried off this Eastern affair to perfection and won a most distinguished position among the European sovereigns."

And in a haze of vicarious glory he read his son, Jean-Baptiste, the following wretched lesson:

"I have just had the honour of having been invited by the Emperor to spend a week with him. Such are the rewards of industry and good behaviour. So you too must work hard, to be rewarded, God willing, in the same way."

Obviously the truth is quite different. At no time was Pasteur's work motivated by the hope of such tawdry "honours" or "rewards". In his letter to his son he was merely echoing the trite sentiments on which his own upbringing had been based. This conformism—political, social, patriotic and religious—was something he never succeeded in throwing off. It makes a weird contrast with the independence of his scientific thinking.

"Pasteur's upbringing and education, and his self-imposed way of life", writes René Dubos, "made him behave like a bourgeois, though his underlying temperament was far more adventurous."

Elsewhere Dubos remarks: "Though his work revolutionized the scientific ideas of his time, causing biology to make gigantic strides and completely renovating therapeutic technique, Pasteur was narrow and limited except where that work was concerned; and it is difficult to decide just how far he was conscious of a wish to shed his narrow outlook, or to preserve it intact."

How are we to visualise Pasteur? Must we picture him as a man pulled in opposite directions by conflicting feelings and pressures and dealing with his plight by a kind of resolute indecision? Must we regard this tension of contrary elements, rather than the strain he imposed on his body and mind in solving the scientific problems which he loved, and which relegated all else to the background of his life, as the cause of the malady which struck at him in the prime of life—namely, hemiplegia? It is, after all, no light thing to flee from one's own nature; and the consolations of genius are not necessarily sufficient to make up for the loss of the self that might have been.

Pasteur the man was certainly a mass of contradictions. Much contemporary evidence has come down to us concerning his adult life—his scientific career, his private life and his social contacts (including his contacts in society with a capital S, though these were mostly confined to his visits to the imperial palaces). We are nevertheless entitled to wonder whether we know all the data of the problem, especially those concerning his adolescence. Did he perhaps undergo some deep psychological trauma in early youth, and suffer from some kind of repression ever afterwards?

PASTEUR'S EMOTIONAL LIFE

Pasteur's affection for his family was typical of all his affections outside science; which is to say that he loved them sincerely, but in his own rather narrow, conventional way. Even as a schoolboy he had set himself up as his sisters' mentor. At times he went further, assuming the mantle of the head of the family.

B

Corresponding with his parents about Joséphine, whose school-
ing he had proposed to pay for out of his own pocket, he wrote:

"She must work very hard in the closing months of this year,
and I therefore urge Mamma not to keep sending her out on
errands, shopping and so on; she must be left free to work."

He seems to have had no affairs with women—rather strange
for a student in the Latin Quarter not long after the Murger
period. However, the evidence is not conclusive; it amounts
merely to the fact that no mention of any such affairs is to be
found in his correspondence and in the reminiscences of his
friends and biographers.

When he was appointed professor at Strasbourg, at the age of
twenty-six, he intimated to his father that for the time being at
least he intended to remain a bachelor. His father's reply was:
"You've told us that you won't marry for a long time yet, and
that you'll take one of your sisters to live with you. I hope this
happens, for your sake and even more for theirs; either of them
would find the greatest happiness in such an arrangement."

But only a fortnight after his arrival in Strasbourg, and therefore only a few days after his letter to his father, he came to a
sudden decision and wrote as follows to M. Laurent, Rector of
the University:

"Sir,—A petition of the greatest significance both to myself
and to your family will reach you in a few days, and I therefore
feel it to be my duty to lay before you the following information,
which may help you in reaching a decision, favourable or unfavourable as the case may be.

"My father is a tanner at Arbois, a small town in the Jura.
My sisters are responsible for the domestic and business tasks
formerly carried out by my mother, of whom we were bereft
last May.

"As a family we live comfortably, but have amassed no
wealth. I would put the total value of our estate no higher than
50,000 francs. And for my own part I decided long ago to leave
my share of the eventual inheritance to my sisters. I therefore
have no means of my own. My only resources are an excellent
constitution, a willing spirit and my post at the University.

"Two years ago I finished my course at the École Normale, obtaining my *agrégation* in the physical sciences. Six months later I obtained my doctorate; and I have submitted several papers to the Académie des Sciences, where they were well received, especially the last. The paper in question was the subject of a highly favourable report, which I have the honour of enclosing with this letter.

"Such, sir, is my present position. As for the future, all I can say is that unless my interests undergo a complete change of direction I shall devote myself to chemical research. My ambition is to go back to Paris as soon as my work has made something of a name for me. M. Biot has told me several times that I ought to think seriously of gaining admission to the Institut.* It will be time to think of that again when I have ten or fifteen years' steady work behind me. Ambitious dreams of this kind are common enough; they are certainly not the source of my attachment to pure science.

"My father is coming shortly to Strasbourg to ask you in person, on my behalf, for your daughter's hand. No one here knows anything of the matter and I feel certain, sir, that, should you refuse, your decision will remain secret.

"I was twenty-six on December 27.

"With assurances of loyalty and profound regard, I am, Sir,

"Yours very truly,

"LOUIS PASTEUR."

Marie Laurent was twenty-two. She knew nothing of Pasteur's letter to her father. Her portraits show her as a very serious girl who might well be attractive to a sober, determined young man like her father's subordinate. Her own enthusiasm, however, does not seem to have been great; we find Pasteur, impatient for a reply from the rector, writing to Mme. Laurent:

"I am afraid lest Mlle. Marie pay too much importance to her first impressions, which can only be unfavourable to myself.

*I.e. the Institut de France, and especially the Académie des Sciences, which is one of the five constituent bodies of the Institut. (*Tr.*)

I have none of the qualities which please a young woman; but memory tells me that whenever people have got to know me well they have become fond of me."

Having eventually been given leave to address the young lady directly, he urged her ". . . simply not to judge me too hastily. You might be mistaken. In time you will come to see that, under a cold, shy exterior which doubtless displeases you, there beats a heart which is full of affection for you."

And when Marie had given her consent Pasteur confessed that he had shed tears in the interim:

"I woke up every morning with the thought that you wouldn't return my love, and then I wept! My work means nothing to me—to me, who was so devoted to my crystals that when I went to bed I wished the night was not so long, so that I could get back to work quicker! . . ."

His feelings were deep and real. Pasteur was a conventional man, sometimes an arrogant one, and not always as kind as he has been said to be. But this letter, so far from making us smile, shows us how sensitive a character underlay the harsh exterior.

At the same time it seems that he was somewhat exaggerating the interruption suffered by his work—his letter to Marie is dated April 3, but on the 7th he had a note from Biot, acknowledging receipt of a batch of crystals. Professor R. Dubos comments: "The disturbance of his laboratory work caused by this emotional tremor was only a ripple which did not really disturb the stream of discoveries, and directly after his marriage Pasteur resumed his scientific mission in a conjugal climate which exactly suited it. . . . Mme. Pasteur made it her purpose in life to devote herself to her husband and his scientific ardour, and to shape her whole behaviour in accordance with the aims he had laid down for them both. She had a good deal to put up with: his low pay as a professor, his habit of buying scientific equipment with the extra income received in the form of prizes, his way of coming home from the laboratory with his head full of strange ideas, and the undeniable fact that work mattered more to him than anything else in the world."

To which we may add the account by Roux: "The first few

days of their life together were enough to tell Mme. Pasteur
what sort of man she had married. She made it her business to
shield him from the practical difficulties of life, assuming
responsibility for all household cares and leaving him free to
concentrate entirely on research. Her love for him included an
understanding of his work. In the evenings she used to write at
his dictation; she spurred him to explain himself more clearly;
she was genuinely interested in hemihedral facets and attenuated viruses, and she had realised that anyone's ideas are made
clearer by his being forced to express them, and that the
greatest stimulus to thinking of new experiments is to have to
describe those you have just been carrying out. She was not
only the ideal wife for him; she was also the best of his scientific
collaborators."

It is highly probable that he had no intimate relationships
with women before he met Marie Laurent, and quite certain
that he had none thereafter, for he abominated adultery and
regarded it as the ultimate in human baseness. On one occasion,
being at a loss for words with which to damn an adversary with
sufficient force, he exclaimed: "That man would do anything
—it wouldn't even surprise me to hear that he was deceiving
his wife!"

THE PUGNACIOUS CONTROVERSIALIST

In Pasteur we see virtually two men. There was the scientist
methodically climbing the rungs of the ladder of knowledge,
making his way from one convincing experiment to the next
and never tolerating, either in others or himself, the slightest
deviation from scientific consistency. And there was the other
Pasteur, tormentedly anxious for his own onward march in the
world, and for his family's, and, on occasion, for that of all mankind. Preoccupations like these do not mix well. The first
engenders selfishness; the second, family ambition; and the
third, a lofty sense of the duty of the human species as such.

Pasteur was neither an egoist nor an individualist. He was a
simple character and not without a streak of kindness. He was
not proud: he was aware of his own worth (a very different

matter). Pride leads to conceit; its possessor tends to develop an unlimited belief in his own qualities and abilities, to imagine himself everybody's superior and to regard the highest honours and rewards as being merely his just deserts. Pasteur, on the other hand, was capable of being naïvely astonished by his own powers. Loir has described how on one occasion Pasteur, meditatively thumbing the pages of the printed collection of his own papers, turned to him and said, "This is good stuff, you know; and it's all mine!... What things there are in it!" This is not the way a conceited man talks. Pasteur's attitude towards himself and his fellows was too honourable for him ever to indulge in cheap boasting. It is true he demanded respect—less, though, as an individual than as a representative of science.

A staff writer on the newspaper *Le Temps* wrote an account of an international medical conference, and concluded his article with a few thoughts of his own; one of these was to the effect that even great intellects, "including such eminent men as M. Pasteur and Mr. Tyndall", were not immune against error. Pasteur's reaction, though it may seem to be a little more than life-size, makes it clear that in defending his own reputation he was chiefly concerned to defend science itself:

To the Editor.

"Sir,—I cannot accept the assertions made by your correspondent, who would do well to render both science and myself the service of publishing, either in your own pages or in the transactions of one of the Académies, the errors to which he alludes. As for his assurance that men accustomed to the rigour of scientific laws and of exact experimentation always commit grave errors when they investigate problems as complex as those of physiology and medicine, I have never heard such a paradoxical statement before, and one so little in harmony with the new spirit which now auspiciously animates the medical sciences. For my own part, I think I may fairly say that my familiarity with laboratory work and with the methods of exact research has enabled me to investigate certain questions in physiology and medicine, despite their complexity, and to clarify them *without any error whatsoever* [Pasteur's italics]. The article to which this is a rejoinder raises at once an issue of personalities and one of method. The latter, rather than the former, makes me feel it my duty to take up my pen, and to request your kindness in publishing my letter as soon as may be."

Pasteur "felt it his duty" to engage in a surprisingly large number of controversies, sometimes on rather childish grounds. Nearly all his polemical writings breathe a high and ardent seriousness, totally devoid of humour; but, as the following letter shows, he was not incapable of wielding the weapon which, in our own day, contributes so much to the attractiveness of the disputes carried on by such British scientists as Haldane. Here is Pasteur's reply to a certain Marquis de Brimard, whose incompetence to treat of the matter under discussion was equalled only by the complacency with which he treated it:

"My Lord Marquis,—I have read your initial letter, published in the *Moniteur des Soies* ['The Silk Review'], on the investigations which I have been carrying out for the last four years in the South of France; and also your subsequent and no less animated letter, which appeared on October 5 of this year [1868] in M. Barral's *Journal de l'Agriculture*.

"If statements derived their validity from the confidence with which they were uttered, rather than from proof, no one would be found to have carried the art of reasoning to a higher pitch than yourself. But those unhappy creatures called scientists, 'those gentlemen' (as you say) whom you treat in so cavalier a fashion, who err so palpably, and who can be credited at most with good intentions, are presumptuous enough to ask for something more impressive by way of logic.

"Allow me to say, my Lord Marquis, entirely without animus, and with the same deference for your position as I am sure you entertain towards mine, that you know nothing whatsoever about my investigations and the deductions arising from them, or the irrefutable principles which they have brought to light, or the practical importance they have already been found to possess. Most of my accounts of them you have left unread; and you have failed to understand the few which you did read.

"Permit me therefore, as a mark of my admiration, to send you copies of all the Reports submitted by me to the Minister of Agriculture in 1867 and 1868, and of my two letters on the *morts-flats* disease,* from the *Transactions of the Académie des Sciences*, June, 1867.

"May I suggest that you read these little works with some small fraction of the care that went into the making of them; and that, having pondered and understood them, you write once more to the *Moniteur des Soies*, giving your impressions and criticisms? If I find that my pupil has made satisfactory progress, I shall be willing to argue with him. As things stand at present we should be fighting with unequal weapons, a proceeding unworthy of a gentleman.

"Allow me to remain
"Your Lordship's most obedient servant,
"L. PASTEUR.
"*Member of the Académie des Sciences*."

It may be safely surmised that, if ridicule could kill, the ignorant Marquis would not have survived this well-earned reproof.

But Pasteur did not always show to such advantage. In the *affaire de l'École Normale* we see him openly misusing his authority.

THE ÉCOLE NORMALE EPISODE

Pasteur had been appointed Director of Scientific Studies, and also Administrator, at the École Normale. Biot had hoped that he would keep his secondary functions within reasonable bounds and had even said: "They've made him Administrator; let them believe that he will administer." But Pasteur's attitude was different; he took both sides of his post seriously and, without letting up on his research work, flung himself into such

---

* Also known as *morts-blancs*, or *maladies des tripes* ("intestinal disease"), or (most commonly) *flacherie*. The silkworm disease which Pasteur was originally invited to investigate was *pébrine*; while he was about it he also dealt with *flacherie*. In both cases he devised successful preventive measures. (*Tr.*)

matters of detail as the number of ounces of meat to be given to each student per day, or the question of whether or not the courtyard should be sanded. Having taken on the job, he was determined to discharge all the responsibilities it involved.

The time came when a minor incident developed into a major collision between him and those under his care. A few score inhabitants of St. Étienne had felt called upon to protest when the two public libraries in their town had acquired copies of supposedly "subversive" works by Voltaire, Rousseau, Renan, Proudhon and others. The "establishment" figures of the day, as might have been expected, sided with the forces of convention and demanded that these "satanic" books be withdrawn by Government decree. This attack on intellectual freedom was welcomed almost without exception by the members of the Senate, who were under the Imperial thumb. One of the few voices raised against it was that of Sainte-Beuve, who had to endure various vicious attacks in consequence, and was even challenged to a duel, a provocation which he very sensibly declined, regarding it as a "summary jurisprudence which consists of stifling a question by suppressing a man". The students of the École Normale supported him: "This is not the first time we have thanked you for defending freedom of thought when it was ignored or attacked; and now that you have pleaded once more on its behalf we offer you renewed thanks." They simultaneously sent out a notice to the Press; Étienne Arago considered it more striking than those the *Moniteur* had so far published on the same subject, and gave it wide publicity.

But university regulations forbade students to take part in political activity of any kind. Nisard, as Director of the École Normale, expelled the student who had signed the letter; Pasteur took his stand on the side of authority and refused to hear anything of clemency or compromise. All students who supported the signatory of the letter were, like him, expelled.

"Pasteur," writes M. René Valléry-Radot, "was a soldier's son and had been brought up to respect discipline. He entirely lacked the arts of dissipating a difficult situation with a word in season and of nipping dissension in the bud with a smile. In science he was a great revolutionary; in social matters he was a devoted adherent of the conventional hierarchy."

PASTEUR AND HIS ASSISTANTS

The legend of Pasteur's kindness cannot have been without a foundation in fact. But the time and money with which to turn his kindness to practical effect were often lacking. And it must be admitted that, on the whole, he was not the man to make life easy either for others or for himself. In pursuit of his goal—which, as we have said, was almost entirely identified with the goals of science itself—he made use of other people, ruling them severely but justly, and even sometimes paying tribute to their talent, but never really seeing them as people, never entering their personal lives or admitting them into his own. "He kept us at a distance from his thoughts", states Duclaux, one of his principal and most highly esteemed assistants. This close disciple also speaks of the "Olympian silence" in which the master shrouded himself. Professor Dubos says he "kept his assistants completely ignorant of the strategy of his research, telling them only as much from day to day as they needed to know for their own tasks". These tasks, another commentator emphasises, were apportioned "curtly, without elaboration". These statements are confirmed by Loir, his technical assistant: "He kept to himself in his laboratory and said nothing about the purpose of what he was doing. He would thumb the pages of his notebook and, on little cards, write down what was to be done; we then had to carry out the necessary experiments, without further explanation."

Pasteur's lack of interest in the people working for him was such that several of them lost heart and left him. But we must be careful not to misjudge him. It was not disdain or conceit or selfishness which made Pasteur behave like this; he simply did not know he was doing it. The great astronomer Le Verrier having complained of the lack of attachment his assistants showed towards him, Pasteur accused him of treating them like machines—and would doubtless have been much astonished to hear that the compliment could have been returned. The fact was that he was entirely absorbed in his work. When an experiment was in progress nothing else was of any importance: "Any interruption caused him real pain", says Émile Roux; "I can see him turn to his interrupter, with a wave of the hand as if to dismiss him, and imploring him in desperate tones, 'No, not now. I'm much too busy.' "

Roux goes on to say: "He was really the simplest, most approachable of men, but incapable of understanding how anyone could interrupt a scientist busy making notes in the laboratory. When Chamberland and I were carrying out an interesting experiment, he used to mount guard over us, keeping watch through the glass-panelled door for any of our colleagues who might come to ask how things were getting on; he himself went out and turned them away."

It must be remembered that, from his forty-sixth year, Pasteur's hemiplegia made it almost impossible for him to handle scientific apparatus himself, so that for the most part he had to content himself with watching experiments for which he had given directions, instead of carrying them out himself. On these occasions his assistants really were no more than extensions of his own powerless hands, while his brain, which was as alert as ever, remained concentrated exclusively on the experiment. Whether he was performing it himself or others were doing it for him, Pasteur forgot everything else for the time being; forgot scientific meetings, forgot even food and drink. Mme. Pasteur had to remind him of her existence and even, in a sense, of his own. Writing to her children, in 1884, she said: "Your father is as preoccupied as ever; he hardly speaks to me, sleeps little, and rises at dawn; in short, he is leading the same life as I began sharing with him, thirty-five years ago today."

PASTEUR AND THE MEDICAL PROFESSION

Where doctors were concerned, Pasteur did not always show much understanding; and the doctors repaid him with interest. He had no medical degree himself; probably some sort of inferiority feeling lay behind his hostility towards them. This amounted almost to systematic opposition, and was carried to great lengths. Grancher, for instance, showed courage and industry as his assistant when his anti-rabies vaccine was being tried out for the first time on human subjects; but Pasteur took him to task for having two armchairs (one of them a rocking chair, which made it worse!) in the annexe a short distance away from the École Normale. Pasteur had relegated him to the annexe "so as to avoid contaminating the peaceful atmosphere of the laboratory with the agitation of medical life" (Dubos). Loir says: "He couldn't understand why anyone should want to have comfortable seats in a laboratory. . . . He was merely confirmed in his belief that the Rue d'Ulm must remain barred to anyone capable of such an attitude to life."

The equally constant antagonism displayed towards him by many doctors sprang from the same trivial cause as his own envy of them: he had not pronounced the Hippocratic oath— he did not possess the talisman of a medical degree. To them he was an ignorant chemist who had dared to invade their noble art; they could not forgive him for overshadowing them by the scope of his work, and for showing up their mistaken ideas with the assurance gained from his strict adherence to sound experimental method.

He was deeply irritated by the pride of some of them, and by the pompous language under which they concealed their mediocrity; so deeply, indeed, that when the most enlightened physicians of the day had insisted on his election to the Académie de Médecine, against obscurantist opposition, he showed his usual utter lack of diplomacy by declaring to that body, in full session:

"You have been asking yourselves by what methods we of the Académie de Médecine can ensure that a truly scientific spirit becomes predominant in our discussions and other activities. Allow me to indicate the method which would certainly not be a panacea, but in which nevertheless I have the greatest confidence. It would consist of a moral undertaking, to be entered upon by each one of us, never to refer to our meeting-place as a *tribunal*, never to refer to any oral communication made here as a *speech*, and never to refer to any of the speakers as an *orator*. Let us leave the use of these expressions to political assemblies, the subject-matter of whose debates usually lies in realms where proof is difficult or impossible. These three words, *tribunal, speech, orator*, seem to me incompatible with the simplicity and rigour of science."

According to Roux, Pasteur was often cross when he came away from a session of the Académie de Médecine: " 'Did you hear about it?' he would say. 'When you describe an experiment, they refute it by making speeches.' " But, adds the illustrious commentator, he gradually calmed down and planned new experimental demonstrations of his discoveries, "since contradiction always spurred him to further research". Not until his jubilee, in 1892, in the speech delivered by his son (he himself being now unhappily incapable of utterance), did he offer something like an apology: "If at times I have disturbed the calm of your sessions by arguing in a somewhat lively strain, the reason was that I was passionately defending the truth."

It is because he was passionately defending truth, or what he believed was truth, that Pasteur refused to make any show of diplomacy or compromise; and it is for the same reason that, while we may dislike certain aspects of his non-scientific life, such as his chauvinism and his relations with Napoleon III, it is impossible not to respect and even venerate him. Where he went wrong about medicine was in not realising the human part played by the doctor, who may make an incorrect diagnosis and yet achieve useful therapeutic results by the very confidence he inspires in the mind of the patient—an old lesson we are learning again today from psychosomatic medicine (obviously, however, only in cases where there is no characteristic infection or mechanical damage).

But there were some doctors whom he was doubtless very right to distrust—the kind whom Claude Bernard, himself a doctor, enjoyed making fun of: "Have you noticed that whenever a doctor enters a drawing-room or arrives at a meeting, he looks as if he was saying, 'I've just saved a human life'?"

Medicine in those days was largely a matter of hit or miss. Pasteur had good reason to preach the doctrine of asepsis. Dangerous germs were often transmitted by dirty dressings.

Sédillot wrote: "Hundreds and thousands of patients, their faces wan, yet still alight with hope and the will to live, died of hospital gangrene sometime between the seventh and fourteenth day. So many failures in the surgery of the past become comprehensible in the light of the germ theory."

Lister, the pioneer of antiseptic methods in surgery, openly declared himself a follower of Pasteur. From 1867 onwards he used a new procedure in the treatment of wounds, aiming to destroy pathogenic bacilli with carbolic acid. Writing to Pasteur, whom he looked on as his master, he said: "If ever you come to Edinburgh, I think you will find it truly rewarding to walk round our hospital and see how greatly mankind is benefiting from your work. Need I add how great a satisfaction I would derive myself from showing you how much the art of surgery is in your debt?"

Of course, Pasteur was not always right in his battle with the doctors. But he was right in the main. Surprisingly, one still comes across doctors who are against him; they are exceedingly few, and not one of them has been able to give me a genuinely scientific reason for his attitude.

PASTEUR'S RELIGION

Roman Catholics have often tried to make out that Pasteur belonged in their camp. So have wine-drinkers, for that matter. But though Pasteur was not a materialist and probably believed in God, he was not a practising worshipper. His family and descendants, who certainly cannot be accused of supporting atheism, have indignantly opposed the Church's attempt to exploit his name, and honest Catholic writers have always been ready to agree with them. It is true he died holding a crucifix in one hand; but he was totally paralysed and the crucifix was placed in his unresisting fingers either by Mme.

Pasteur or by some other member of the family, all of whom were very devout. Can we really attribute much significance to what happens in the hour of death, when the last remnants of the sufferer's intellectual faculties are at grips with the terrifying mystery of life and its extinction? And does the crucifix, the symbol of Christ—the Man who died because He preached the doctrine of universal love among men—belong only to organised religion?

Pasteur, according to his granddaughter, Mme. Camille Vallery-Radot, regarded sincerity as the highest virtue and deceit as the most odious of vices; he is entitled, surely, to have the truth told about his death, as about his life. M. Pasteur Vallery-Radot, in *Pasteur Inconnu* ("The Unknown Pasteur"), writes with understandable anger that "to try to enrol Pasteur under one doctrinal banner or another is a mark of intellectual dishonesty". He points out that his mother, René Vallery-Radot's wife, Pasteur's daughter and a devout practising Catholic, "but of an honesty equal to Pasteur's own", never let anyone misrepresent her father's position: he was not an atheist or a materialist, but that was all that could be said; he was without any sectarian attachment.

Again, Professor Pasteur Vallery-Radot wrote in 1939 to M. Paul Dupuy: "My father, and my mother too, always made it clear that Pasteur was not a practising religionist. If you look at his *Life of Pasteur* you will see that my father always refers to Pasteur's outlook as basically religious, but never as Catholic. I can well remember my parents' indignation whenever some priest in his pulpit quoted a sentence which in fact Pasteur never uttered: 'I have the faith of a Breton charcoal-burner.'" In the same letter, M. Pasteur Vallery-Radot expressly says: "Everything which has been written about the supposed Catholicism of Pasteur is completely untrue."

Even a churchman, Mgr. Dubourg, Archbishop of Besançon, has declared from his pulpit: "Pasteur was a believer, but not, in the full sense of the word, a practising one." And M. André Georges (from whom we have borrowed most of these quotations so as not be be accused of using anti-Catholic sources) ends the first part of his chapter on Pasteur's religion with the unequivocal statement: "He proclaimed more than once that his ideal was 'evangelical'—an ideal of which his perfect Christian wife was a constant example; but the greater part of his life—that is to say, all of it except his childhood and his last six months—gives us no justification for regarding him as a real Catholic, still less as a 'Catholic scientist'."

For something like a definitive profession of Pasteur's faith, made when his fame was at its height and his faculties were still unimpaired, we can turn to the words he spoke at the graveside of Henry Sainte-Claire Deville in 1881: "The idea of God is a form of the idea of the infinite. As long as mankind stands in awe of the infinite, temples will be raised for its worship, whether the name of God be Brahma, Allah, Jehovah or Jesus."

This leaves no room for confusion: Pasteur extolled the religious spirit in general, but supported no particular sect.

3

Pasteur the Genius

IN October, 1872, Pasteur returned for the second time to Paris, "this city which, from any point of view, is both beautiful and ugly at once", as he wrote to his father: "Here more than anywhere we see vice and virtue, honesty and dishonesty, riches and poverty, perpetually colliding and interweaving." He added: "But one can remain simple and upright in heart, here as well as anywhere; only those without will-power allow themselves to change."

He himself had come to Paris with his mind strongly made up: he was going to enter the École Normale. But this was something of which he did not yet feel himself "worthy", as he put it, as he was only fifteenth in the list of successful candidates; he therefore began by entering the Lycée Saint-Louis and also attended lectures assiduously at the Sorbonne, especially those of Dumas, who had become Professor of Chemistry in succession to Gay-Lussac.

At the Lycée he was awarded two distinctions and a first prize in physics at the end of the academic year in 1843, and finished sixth (likewise in physics) in the *concours général*.* On his second attempt at the entrance examination of the École Normale he was placed fourth, which he felt gave him the right to realise his ambition.

* The *concours général* is an annual nation-wide competition for all pupils in the highest forms in French secondary schools who have finished top in one or more of the principal academic subjects. (*Tr.*)

From now onwards he progressed with giant strides. His scientific career falls into three main periods. The first was exclusively physico-chemical, being devoted to crystallography; the second was biological and led to the overthrow of the spontaneous generation theory (such generation being shown not to exist in any circumstances now known, under natural conditions); the third was marked by the founding of a new science, micro-biology, which was destined to split into bacteriology and virology (the study, respectively, of bacteria and of viruses) and subsequently to lead to immunology.

Of course, this is a formal division only; there was in fact no break between the periods. And in addition Pasteur made a sally from time to time into the domain of the practical, most notably with pasteurisation and the study of silkworm diseases. Through the diversity of his work we can see the following line of development:

(*a*) Having discovered molecular dissymmetry in the course of purely physical and chemical inquiry, he moved directly into biology with an attempt to explain the nature of organic structures, whose mechanisms appeared to be a function of this dissymmetry.

(*b*) Through studying the way in which one of the possible asymmetrical components, rather than another, is developed in a given organism, he was led to the discovery of the micro-organisms responsible for fermentation.

(*c*) His observation that processes of fermentation, and of putrefaction, never took place in the absence of such micro-organisms turned his mind in the direction which led to experimental proof of the fact that life originates only from antecedent life (the germ theory, and rebuttal of the spontaneous generation theory).

(*d*) Having thus refuted, at least in the case of infectious diseases, the contemporary doctrine that disease was "in us, and of us, and brought into being by us", he was in a position to begin the systematic study of the pathogenic agents responsible for infection.

(*e*) The cause of a given disease being now known, it became possible to devise ways of combating or preventing that disease. This phase of Pasteur's work was immensely fruitful from the medical point of view, in that it produced various kinds of inoculation. One eventual result was serum therapy; another was the beginnings of immunology; yet another was the work which led to the creation of antibiotics, the indispensable counterpart to asepsis. (The latter, the discovery of which was entirely due to Pasteur, can only prevent disease from getting in, not fight it once it has entered.)

MOLECULAR DISSYMMETRY

Pasteur frequently told his assistants: "I have no theories—only facts, and conclusions which are adequate to the facts." In all likelihood he had no theories or preconceived ideas when he chose crystallography as the subject of his physics thesis at the École Normale. At that period his only ambition was, in his own words, that of becoming "a distinguished teacher".

But he did want to be something more than just a salaried employee doing his job. He wanted to know and understand as thoroughly as possible the things he was to teach, and even hoped it might be granted to him to make his own contribution to human knowledge; such were the ambitions he confided to his close friend, Chappuis. He begged Dumas to take him on as assistant, "not because of the financial advantage the post might confer, or because it would enable him to make influential friends, but because he might conceivably have a chance of making original discoveries and because, at the least, he would be improving his ability as a teacher". In his student days he never thought of himself as destined for an outstanding career or even as being specially talented, nor were other people any more prescient: the official report on him at the École Normale stated laconically: "He should be an excellent teacher."

Crystallography was only a tiny part of the enormous programme of instruction offered by the École Normale. What made Pasteur turn to it in 1844, when he was looking for a subject for his thesis? His own account was that he was "attracted by the subtle and delicate methods used in studying these beautiful crystalline forms". His boyhood love of drawing comes out here; another influence must have been that of Delafosse, his Professor of Mineralogy, who had followed up the pioneer work achieved by Haüy in the domain of crystallography.

The scientific study of crystals was still in its infancy. It had occurred to the British astronomer John Herschel to study in combination two sets of results which had been achieved separately: namely, the purely crystallographical observations made by Haüy and Delafosse; and the discovery made by the physicist Jean-Baptiste Biot, that if polarised light is shone through a quartz crystal in line with the crystal's major axis the plane of the light is rotated through a certain distance (*see* below). In addition, Haüy, and later Delafosse, had pointed to certain variations in the direction of the inclination of some of the facets of quartz crystals. Evidently there was a cause-and-effect relationship at work which demanded elucidation.

CRYSTALLOGRAPHY AND POLARISATION

The idea of crystalline structure is a very ancient one. The natural philosophers of ancient Greece, those "explorers of the universe", paid some attention to the various forms of pyrite crystals. Leaving questions of substance aside and concentrating solely on form, they identified the five regular polyhedra: tetrahedron, cube, octahedron, dodecahedron, icosahedron. But crystallography as a branch of scientific investigation did not really begin till the middle of the eighteenth century, when Romé de l'Isle decided to study the property possessed by various minerals, of assuming forms bounded by plane surfaces whose intersections are straight lines.

Modern research has established the fact that the external form of any crystal is due to an ordered arrangement of atoms, molecules or ions within the bulk of the solid. The "internal image" of any crystalline form can be obtained by techniques making use of X-rays, infra-red rays and, in the case of transparent crystals, the wavelengths of visible light. It is now known that almost all solids possess a crystalline structure; a gas, on the other hand, is disorderly, a random assembly of molecules; liquids are somewhat less disorderly—some of them possess a crystalline structure.

In 1815 Haüy enunciated the *law of rational intercepts*, which states that the edges (the lines between adjacent faces) of any crystalline form are intersected in rational ratios by the faces of another form belonging to the same system. These ratios being limited in number, the number of possible crystal-forms is also limited.

Another fact demonstrated by Haüy is that the nucleus of a crystal, that is to say the initial molecule on the lines of which the crystalline mass of a given solid is built up, is a polyhedron similar to those obtained by *cleavage* of a crystal. Crystals can be shattered more easily in some directions than others; cleavage consists of splitting a crystal along these natural lines of division, the end-result being the *cleavage nucleus* of the crystal. It should be noted, however, that the parallel between the cleavage nucleus and the structure of the molecule applies only to crystals having three cleavage planes—this being a necessary condition for obtaining a nucleus by mechanical division.

Crystalline forms are extremely varied. Some are symmetrical, others only partly so; one variety of zincblende (zinc sulphide) crystal, for example, consists of two tetrahedra, the faces of one of which are smooth and shimmering whereas those of the other are striated and dull. Partially symmetrical crystals are called merohedral and are geometrically classified in accordance with the degree of merohedry they display: they are hemihedral, tetartohedral or ogdohedral, in accordance as they possess half, or a quarter, or an eighth of the elements of symmetry of the lattice of the type to which they belong. (The "lattice" is the regular three-dimensional array of the atoms in a crystal.)

There are several different classes of hemihedry; one of the most important is that possessing the property of *enantiomorphism*. Two figures, or polyhedra, or crystals, are enantiomorphic if each can be considered as the mirror-image of the other, with this vital difference: neither can be superimposed on the other. They have the same elements (edges, dihedral angles, etc.) but these elements are placed in the opposite order in the one to what they are in the other.

POLARISED LIGHT AND THE ROTATION OF ITS PLANE

What is polarised light? and how does it occur?

Our description will necessarily be crude and summary; a more technical account would fill many pages and would be hard going for the non-scientific reader.

Light is transmitted from a source (the sun, a lamp, a lighted match or what you will) in the form of what is known as transverse waves.* Each of the vibrations of which these waves consist can be resolved into two components, one at right angles to the other. In certain circumstances (named below) one of these components is eliminated; the light is then said to be *polarised*. And the plane of the remaining component (the one not eliminated) is known as the *plane of polarisation*.

Polarised light was observed for the first time by Bartholinus in 1669, the polarisation being caused in this case by *double refraction*. Another cause is *selective absorption*: certain substances (including many natural crystals) affect light passing through them, one of the two components in each vibration being arrested and the other allowed to pass through; in other words, the light is polarised. This happens because of the internal molecular structure of the substance concerned. The third way polarised light is produced is by *reflection*; light is polarised if it is reflected from a plane sheet of glass, or any other suitable surface, at an angle of incidence of about 56°. The phenomenon was discovered in 1808 by the French physicist Malus; while on a visit to Paris he looked through an Iceland spar crystal at the sunlight reflected from the windows of the Palais du Luxembourg, and found that if he rotated the crystal slowly there was one position in which only one image could be seen (in all

* Transverse waves: those in which the particles of the vibrating medium move transversely to the direction of propagation (e.g. water waves). Longitudinal waves: the particles move in line with the direction of propagation (e.g. sound waves).

other positions of the crystal he "saw double", because Iceland spar causes double refraction). This could only mean that the light was polarised; and further investigation showed that it was so.

Malus's discovery stimulated research. Arago resumed his own studies of light. The phenomenon of *rotary polarisation* was discovered: it was found that some substances had the property of rotating, through a fixed angle, the plane of a beam of polarised light which was made to pass through them. The angle varies from one substance to another; so does the direction of rotation, substances which make the plane deviate to the right or left being known respectively as dextro-rotatory and laevo-rotatory, or simply as right-handed and left-handed. Substances possessing this property are called "optically active". The rotation of the plane is different for the different colours (wavelengths) of which light is composed; this is the phenomenon known as "optical scattering".

PASTEUR AND DISSYMMETRY

"One day", writes Pasteur, "it happened that M. Laurent, who was studying, if I remember rightly, a specimen of perfectly crystallised tungstate of soda, showed me with the help of his microscope that this salt, though apparently very pure, was clearly a mixture of three different kinds of crystals which anyone with a little familiarity with crystalline forms could recognise without difficulty. This instance, and several others of the same kind, made it clear to me how greatly chemistry could be assisted by a knowledge of crystalline forms. The lessons of our modest and excellent professor of mineralogy, M. Delafosse, had long made me feel attracted towards crystallography. . . . I began making a careful study of a very beautiful series of compounds, all of which crystallise readily—namely, tartaric acid and the tartrates."

Biot had discovered the fact that tartaric acid—an organic substance, like sugar, camphor, and turpentine, has the property of rotating the plane of polarised light in the same way as quartz. But quartz displays this quality only in the crystalline state, whereas tartaric acid does it both in the liquid state and in solution.

Pasteur therefore knew that the optical properties of organic substances arose from their molecular structure, whereas those of inorganic substances, such as quartz, depend on their crystalline structure.

In 1844 Mitscherlich, a German chemist, had published a note setting forth some curious observations concerning the tartrates (salts or esters of tartaric acid). At that time, two different forms of tartaric acid were known to develop in the vats where wine was put to ferment: one of them was present in the hard crust of potassium tartrate which builds up on the inside of the vat during fermentation; the other was derived from this one, among whose large crystals it made its appearance in the shape of slender crystalline needles.

Berzelius had distinguished this secondary form by calling it *paratartaric* acid; Gay-Lussac had preferred the term *racemic* acid because it owed its origin to the grape (Latin, *racemus*).

"The two forms of tartaric acid and their respective salts, the tartrates and the paratartrates", Mitscherlich had written, "possess the same chemical composition, the same crystalline form, with the same angles, the same specific gravity, the same double refraction and, therefore, the same angles between their optical axes. When dissolved in water they display the same refraction, but whereas a tartrate rotates the plan of polarised light, a paratartrate does not."

A challenge indeed! Why should chemically identical substances behave differently in relation to polarised light, one being "active" and the other "inactive"? It was obvious to Pasteur that there must be a reason for this difference; but what was it? Setting aside the chemical aspect of the question, he began studying the crystalline forms of tartrate and para-tartrate, and tartaric and paratartaric acid. At once he noticed something which nobody else had hit upon: tartrate crystals possessed small secondary facets similar to those of quartz, that is to say they were situated on one side of the crystal only.

Tartrate crystals rotated polarised light in that direction, as

Mitscherlich had said. From this, Pasteur concluded that a crystal's form and its optical properties were closely connected. This was as true of quartz as it was of the tartrates. The difference was that the latter retained their optical qualities when in solution, whereas the former rotated polarised light only if it was still in the crystalline state.

Tartaric acid crystals are dissymmetrical. This, declared Pasteur, with all the self-confidence of youth and enthusiasm, must be at least part of the reason for their effect on polarised light. Logically, therefore, paratartrate crystals must be symmetrical: either they must possess no secondary facets at all, or else these facets must be symmetrically paired. But, to his vast disappointment, he found that paratartrates, like tartrates, had dissymmetrical facets.

A less determined character would have given way to discouragement. But Pasteur had made up his mind: there must be a difference, and he was going to find it. And suddenly a curious feature caught his eye: in the tartrates, the facets were inclined to the right, relatively to the principal faces of the crystal; but in the paratartrates they were inclined to the right in some crystals, *and to the left in others*. The thought then struck him that it was the mixture of the two sorts of crystal which cancelled the rotatory effect on polarised light in the case of the paratartrates, both in crystalline form and in solution. Patiently he separated out the two kinds of crystal, one by one; next, since there was no need to reconstitute a single large crystal out of each heap of little crystals, he made two solutions in water— one of the crystals whose facets were inclined to the left, and the other of those whose facets were inclined to the right; after which he hurried to the polariscope and, with understandable anxiety, tested his hypothesis. And he found it was correct: the solution of right-handed crystals turned the plane of the polarised light to the right, and the solution of left-hand crystals turned it to the left.

He lost no time in taking an equal weight of both solutions, mixing them, and testing them with the polariscope. His expectations were confirmed: the new solution was optically inactive.

HIS FIRST TRIUMPH

Vallery-Radot describes how Pasteur, unable to contain his enthusiasm, strode out of the laboratory in the École Normale. In one of the corridors he met a laboratory assistant, whom he dragged out into the Luxembourg Gardens and told of his exploit. News of his experiment soon spread through scientific circles in Paris. Balard told Dumas, and subsequently Biot, who had devoted his life to crystallography and was somewhat sceptical of the results attained by this young scientist from the provinces. In the words of Pasteur himself:

"He asked me to his house and made me repeat the crucial experiment in his presence. He handed me some paratartaric acid which he had prepared himself with special care, and which he had found to be completely neutral with regard to polarised light. He watched me as I prepared from it a double salt with soda and ammonia, these materials also being supplied by him. The liquid was left to evaporate slowly in one of his rooms, and when it had yielded some 30 or 40 grammes of crystals he asked me to accompany him to the Collège de France, where I was to sort them out into two groups according to their crystallographic characteristics; he also asked me to declare afresh that, in my belief, the crystals I placed on his right would make polarised light deviate to the right, and those on his left to the left. When I had done so, he said he would look after the rest of the experiment himself. He prepared the two solutions at the appropriate strength, and when the time came to examine them with the polariscope he invited me into the room again. The first solution he placed in the apparatus was the more interesting one, the one which could be expected to make the light deviate leftwards. Without even taking a reading, he was able to see, by comparing the two images shown by the apparatus—the normal one and the rotated— that there was in very fact a marked leftward deviation. And then, visibly excited, this famous old man took me by the arm and said, 'My dear boy, I love science so much, and always have, that this sets my heart pounding.'"

This exclamation makes it quite clear that Biot had no jealous or bitter feelings towards Pasteur. This twenty-six-year-old, who had suddenly become his equal, had in fact confirmed a theory which he had maintained for thirty years, but had never been able to prove—namely, that the study of rotated polarisation provided the most reliable method of exploring the molecular constitution of chemical substances.

Being an astute person, he realised at once that Louis Pasteur had a future; his first discovery would not be his last. Biot was aware of all the pitfalls awaiting a youthful talent in the academic jungle. He became Pasteur's protector and mentor and remained so until his own death in 1862, at the age of eighty-eight. He never flattered him. He was a true friend, ever ready to warn him of the dangers of impatience and over-ambition, and frequently deploring the younger man's tendency to restrict his achievements by pouring out his gifts on too wide a range of subjects.

STEREOCHEMISTRY AND ISOMERISM

In the following year, 1849, Pasteur was appointed professor of physics at the Faculty of Natural Sciences in Strasbourg. There, as we know, he met Marie Laurent, daughter of the Dean of the Faculty, and tore himself away from his microscope just long enough to marry her. Only a few days after the wedding he was as busy as before, investigating the relationships between a substance's chemical composition, its crystalline form, and its effect on polarised light. He had started by showing that whereas tartrates and paratartrates consisted essentially, as Mitscherlich had stated, of the same kinds of atoms and the same numbers of those atoms in each case, this identity did not apply to the way the atoms were arranged in the molecules of the two substances respectively.

For five years (1848-53) he worked on the problem of the isomerism of the tartaric acids and substances derived from them, laying solid foundations for a new scientific discipline, *stereochemistry*, the study of the spatial arrangement of atoms in the structure of the molecule.

Almost without exception, the molecules of which organic matter is built up are dissymmetrical. The aminoacids, the fundamental "bricks" of organic matter, are either right-handed or left-handed—that is to say, they make the plane of polarised light deviate either to the right or to the left. But all the amino-acids occurring in the proteins of living creatures are left-handed (except those found in certain bacteria—and these amino-acids appear to be unassimilable by living things). As Pasteur showed, if a substance contains both left-handed and right-handed molecules, it is impossible to separate one kind from the other: this sorting-out always presupposes the intervention of life.

Life is capable of synthesising dissymmetrical molecules; human methods are not. Artificial synthesis in the laboratory always produces optically inactive compounds.

The reason is simple: the means employed to produce the necessary reactions (heat, light, filtration, distillation, congelation, and so forth) include no inherent factor of dissymmetry; hence it is statistically inevitable that they will produce left-handed and right-handed molecules in equal quantities.

Organic reactions, on the contrary, precisely because the molecules of organic substances are essentially dissymmetrical, tend to produce dissymmetrical substances. And if racemic substances are made available to an organism (assuming, of course, the organism to be one whose metabolism is capable of dealing with laboratory organic substances), it tends to use an enantiomorphic form of those substances, and to reject the rest.

HUNTING FOR PARATARTRATE

Paratartaric acid was of recent discovery (1820). It had been found by an industrialist of Thann (Haut-Rhin) and appeared to "arise incidentally in the formation of tartaric acid". At the time when it caused such a stir it was no longer easily come by; in France, it was nowhere to be had. So Pasteur, much harassed by want of money, had to look for it all over central Europe; the only reward for his efforts was the certainty that the elusive substance was always present in the mother-liquor after the

raw tartrates had been extracted. It had been gradually eliminated from tartaric acid properly so called, and only some
lucky technical trick would enable it to be produced in quantity. But what was the trick?

In 1828 Berzellius, analysing the two acids, tartaric and paratartaric, and noting their complete identity from the chemical
point of view, had been forced to conclude that if tartaric acid
was optically active and paratartaric was inactive, the difference must be caused by some physical phenomenon.

Chemical identity means that the molecules consist of the
same numbers of atoms of the same elements. Physical identity
would mean that these atoms were situated at exactly the same
points in space in relation one to another. There must therefore
be substances, Berzelius concluded, "which are composed of
the same number of simple atoms, yet possess different properties". Today we call them *isomers*; Berzelius called them
"isomeric".

In 1874 the disposition of the atoms in a molecule (in other
words, their relative positions in three-dimensional space) was
mapped for the first time. The chemical formula for a given
substance (the numbers of atoms of the various elements of
which a given compound consists) can be so depicted in three-
dimensional space as to give an exact representation of a molecule of that substance, not only chemically but physically. This
is stereochemistry. At the time, one of the outstanding conclusions arrived at by research was that "every carbon compound which, in solution, causes the plane of the polarisation
of light to deviate, contains an asymmetrical carbon—that is, a
carbon atom bonded to four different radicals".

Pasteur came back from his European wanderings without
having discovered how paratartaric acid was formed. But he
did know that it was theoretically possible to obtain inactive
forms from tartaric acid, which contained exactly the same
atoms. Broadly speaking, this meant that the particular spatial
structure composed by these atoms must be broken up and then
rearranged so as to form a non-specific structure.

So that the thing to do was to make these atoms regroup

themselves to a different configuration, forming a substance which did not affect polarised light in place of one which did. This new substance would be a mixture, in equal parts, of right-handed and left-handed tartrate crystals; it would be paratartrate.

It is clear that while Pasteur never held a theory *a priori*, and while he always took his stand on facts, the latter did lead him to formulate theories or hypotheses—which, however, were regarded as valid only if supported by further facts. So there is no contradiction between the sentence quoted early in this chapter ("I have no theories", etc.) and another of his statements: "Without theory, practice is mere routine born of habit. Only theory is capable of exciting and developing the spirit of discovery. . . ."

ORGANIC AND INORGANIC MATTER ARE BUILT OF IDENTICAL COMPONENTS

It was by raising tartrate of cinchonine to a high temperature and keeping it there for several hours that Pasteur succeeded in breaking down the spatial structure of its molecules. The result was a congeries of disorganised molecules. Upon cooling, this mixture of the original components of the tartrate did not regroup preferentially, as in the initial compound which was the product of organic processes, but, as Pasteur had expected, yielded inactive paratartrate, consisting half of right-handed tartrate and half of left-handed (in addition, the paratartaric acid formed in the process gave rise to a mesotartaric acid which could not be decomposed into right- and left-handed acids).

On May 24, Biot received a telegram from Strasbourg: "*Am transforming tartaric acid into racemic. Please inform MM. Dumas and Sénarmont. Louis Pasteur.*" Biot answered briefly but warmly: "*Congratulations. Your discovery is now complete.*"

If he had chosen to halt at this point, Pasteur could have counted on seeing his name shining like a star of the first magnitude in the firmament of discovery. He would have been rewarded with a professorial chair at the Sorbonne and various other worldly advantages. He would have led a calm, placid life, publishing from time to time a "note" addressed to the Académie des Sciences, of which he would have become a member in due course by sheer seniority, his election arousing no jealousy and gaining him no enemies. The "notes" would probably have been written by one or another of his pupils, but what was wrong with that? It would be generally understood that the inspiration behind the work was his, and his signature, above the real author's or authors', would be like a seal ratifying this new accession to his fame.

But Pasteur was not that kind of man. His thirst for knowledge and discovery was as insatiable as his resolution to emerge victorious from every encounter which life might bring. He was ambitious both in a good and in a bad sense. He was an extraordinary mixture of the highest scientific merits and of all-too-human faults—a combination which was to make him one of the most astonishing of all nineteenth-century figures.

After his triumph in 1853, he spent five years experimenting on numerous substances, acquiring an ever-deeper conviction that the components of organic and inorganic matter were totally identical, and continually meeting with the same fundamental characteristic: dissymmetry in the structure of all organic matter and all matter of organic origin. There is no doubt that he was the first observer to see the cosmic significance of this connection between dissymmetry and vital processes. Here is the letter he sent on August 12, 1858, to each of the members of the Académie des Sciences who were serving on the committee of the Prize for Experimental Physiology, an award for which he was competing:

"Do you remember, Sir, the curious structure of paratartaric or racemic acid? I showed, in 1849, that this acid is a combination of one molecule of right-handed tartaric acid (ordinary tartaric acid, that is to say) and one molecule of left-handed tartaric acid, which differs from right-handed only in that their forms, otherwise identical in all respects, cannot be superimposed on one another, and in their power of rotating the plane of polarised light: the deviation in the first case being to the right, and in the second to the left. Each of these acids is the mirror-image of the other.

"You also know, sir, that (apart from a certain class of reactions, to which I shall return in due course) the identity between the chemical properties of these two acids is so perfect that it would be materially impossible to find any difference between them, other than their equal but opposite optical qualities, and their crystalline forms, of which each is exactly the inverse of the other: each being the same in every detail of geometrical configuration, but not susceptible of being super-imposed on the other.

"This is the first known example of two substances, the distinction between which eludes chemical analysis; and which nevertheless must be separated by more than physical differences, since they combine with one another, in definite proportions, in a reaction which produces heat, to form a compound with different properties from those of the original substances.

"If we confine ourselves to this aspect of the discovery of the molecular structure of racemic acid, we shall be in a position to deduce several consequences which I will indicate forthwith, since they are the basis of such further conclusions as I wish to present.

"By obtaining these results Physics puts its finger (if I may so express myself) on the cause of rotated polarisation, which was partially divined by the penetrating genius of Fresnel in the following admirable passage of his *Memorandum on double refraction*: 'Some perfectly crystallised substances, such as rock-crystal, display optical phenomena which cannot be reconciled with complete parallelism of the molecular lines, and which would appear to indicate a progressive, regular deviation of those lines in passing from a section through the mid-point to the next section, and so on.'

"The facts mentioned above in connection with the two kinds of tartaric acid, the dextro-rotatory and laevo-rotatory, leave no room for doubt that, in the very molecules of those acids, there is a dissymmetry whose nature is covered by the mathematical formulation used by Fresnel in his attempt to describe the crystalline structure of quartz."

A few remarks must be interpolated at this point. Asymmetry is not a characteristic only of life. The earth itself, for example, is far from being a perfect sphere. If it were cut into two equal parts, or as nearly equal as possible—into northern and southern hemispheres, or eastern and western for that matter—neither part would be a perfect mirror-image of the other. The sun is asymmetrical too—even were it only by the irregular distribution of sunspots. No star is symmetrical. And, to go further along the macrocosmic scale, all galaxies are dissymmetrical.

If we come down the scale in the opposite direction, we find the same thing. While a given atom can be regarded as the exact replica of another atom and, *a fortiori*, one subatomic or subnuclear particle is the exact replica of another, it is quite clear that the force-effects by which they are grouped into larger structures, are dissymmetrical. Recent work in physics has shown that in certain circumstances (namely interactions involving very low energies) the parity principle (or "mirror theory") can be violated.

Dissymmetry, then, is fundamental to the structure even of the symmetrical components of inorganic matter. The basic structures of matter are "inert" and symmetrical only by virtue of the union of contraries; just as the atom is neutral only because the electromagnetic effects involved in it are complementary to each other. Obviously, the whole problem—which we have only adumbrated here—is endlessly complex.

Pasteur, who discovered the importance of dissymmetry in the dynamics of living form, resolutely tackled the subject from a physical, not a metaphysical, point of view. He proved that there was no fundamental difference between the components of mineral matter and those of organic matter; though in his choice of examples he was limited by the experimental possibilities of the time.

He continued substantially as follows:

"While quartz possesses the two characteristics of dissymmetry, 'hemihedry in the form observed by Haüy and the rotatory phenomenon discovered by Arago', the quartz molecule is entirely lacking in dissymmetry. Allow me to give a simple picture—at bottom, however, a true one—of the difference between the structure of quartz and that of natural organic substances: imagine a spiral staircase whose steps are cubes, or some other shape which permits of superimposition. Destroy the staircase, and you have destroyed the dissymmetry at the same time. The staircase's dissymmetry depended solely on the way in which its individual steps were put together. Quartz is like that. The quartz crystal corresponds to the staircase before destruction. It [the crystal] is hemihedral. Consequently it acts upon polarised light. But if the crystal is dissolved or melted, if its physical structure is destroyed by one means or another, its dissymmetry vanishes and so does its action on polarised light; in the latter respect it behaves like (for example) an alum solution, a liquid consisting of molecules distributed in a random fashion. But now imagine a spiral staircase with irregular tetrahedra for steps. You can destroy the staircase but there will still be dissymmetry, because you will be left with a pile of tetrahedra. They may be lying in all sorts of positions but each of them has its own dissymmetry. The same is the case with any substance of organic origin; each of its molecules is dissymmetrical, and this dissymmetry is reflected in the shape of the crystal. When the crystal is destroyed by dissolution the liquid is active with respect to polarised light because it consists of molecules distributed pell-mell, it is true, but all possessing a dissymmetry which acts in the same direction, though not with the same intensity regardless of position."

This is not the place for a philosophical discussion of the varied effects, and the possible causes, of dissymmetry either in the organic realm or the inorganic. To put it briefly, it is clear that some kind of fundamental dissymmetry is the precondition for the existence of some non-living structures characterised by a tendency towards a static condition, or annihilation, or entropy. Other structures—those characteristic of life—tend to organise themselves in an essentially dynamic condition; the outstanding feature of these arrangements of structure is their ability to reproduce themselves, and their general trend is undoubtedly one of resistance to entropy.

But we must return to Pasteur's letter to the jury of the *Prize for Experimental Physiology*. It provides us with an excellent epitome of the work he did in the ten years from 1848 to 1858: work which led him gradually from physics into chemistry, and from chemistry to the study of previously unexplored reactions which were primarily biological in character:

"In mineralogical studies, hemihedry was at one time no more than a geometrical curiosity. Now, however, it is seen to be intimately connected with the inner structure of the molecule; we find it to be one of the visible manifestations of a structural dissymmetry characterising the smallest particles of matter.*

"As for chemistry, it is concerned in two ways with the discovery of the composition of racemic acid; and it is important to say what these two ways are.

"Never before had the detailed molecular structure of two different substances been more tangibly revealed, both in its nature and in its influence on the physical and chemical properties of matter. Never before had a case of isomerism between two substances been so intelligibly explained.

"At the same time, in view of the absolute identity between the chemical properties of two acids which exert diametrically opposite actions on polarised light, it might well have been thought that affinity, the force by means of which we seek to account for all chemical phenomena,† had nothing to do with the rotation of polarised light or with its cause; such rotation having hitherto been regarded as a physical, not a chemical, phenomenon.

"It was reasonable to argue: 'What difference does it make

* Or at least of such particles as could be regarded as the smallest at the period when Pasteur was writing.

† The notion of affinity has since been rendered more precise in the light of electro-magnetism and electro-magnetic resonance.

if the natural organic substances which are indispensable to life (cellulose, albumen, fibrin, gelatine, sugar, gum, starch, etc.) are dissymmetrical in structure? There is no reason to suppose that this characteristic has any influence on the vital processes in which the substances in question play a part; for even if its direction is reversed, the dissymmetry makes no difference to the chemical characteristics involved.

"This line of thought received apparent confirmation from my work on the inactive form of aspartic and malic acid.* I found that it was possible to deprive a substance of its power to affect polarised light, and of its molecular dissymmetry, without causing any significant modification in its physical or chemical properties.†

"However, it was clear to me that I had so far been comparing the two tartaric acids in a special way; I had, in a sense, considered limiting cases only. I therefore devised new ways of comparing the chemical properties of the two substances; and I was able to watch the molecular dissymmetry which is proper to natural organic matter, actively modifying chemical affinities.

"The following were the circumstances in which this took place. The chemical identity of the two tartaric acids is really not absolute unless a certain condition is fulfilled, and this condition, though it now seems quite obvious, eluded my attention for several years. The two substances must be subjected to actions which are not dissymmetrical: for instance, that of substances which do not affect polarised light. If, on the other hand, they are brought together with substances possessing a molecular dissymmetry similar to their own, their identity disappears completely. The resulting compounds are quite different: in solubility, composition, and the shapes of their crystals. They behave differently when raised to a high temperature. There are even cases in which combination takes

* Aspartic acid is one of the constituents of proteins. Malic acid occurs in fruit juices.

† Both malic and aspartic acid were already being successfully synthesised. In this form, however, they were optically inactive, whereas the natural forms are active.

place with the dextro-rotatory substance, but not with the laevo-rotatory.

"It was on the basis of these results, whose mechanical cause is easily grasped, that I now sought to break down racemic acid, isolating its two components, the dextro- and laevo-rotatory, by a purely chemical means instead of the manual, mechanical method which I had used in my initial researches.

"If we make a quantity of racemate (paratartrate) of cinchonicine (a new alkali, isomeric with cinchonine, and easy to prepare); and if we then crystallise this salt, it will be found that the earlier crystallisations consist of laevo-rotatory cinchonicine tartrate: and the later, of dextro-rotatory.

"Here then we have the rotatory property, or more precisely the molecular dissymmetry which is its cause, playing a direct part in a chemical reaction as a modifier of affinities. This being so, we may justifiably suppose that the molecular dissymmetry of natural organic substances exerts some degree of influence in the physical and chemical phenomena of living processes on every occasion when dissymmetrical action of any kind, known or unknown, is involved."

EXPERIMENTS IN DISSYMMETRY

From this point onwards Pasteur's researches were dominated, as he himself says, "by the thought that the structure of substances, in terms of their molecular symmetry or dissymmetry, must have much to do with the nature of the innermost laws of the structure of living creatures".

He was convinced that the origin of the dissymmetry of the dynamic elements from which all living processes were constituted must be sought in some primary, basic dissymmetry.

"The Universe", he wrote with profound conviction, "is a dissymmetrical whole, and I am persuaded that life, as manifested to us and observed by us, is directly or indirectly a function of the dissymmetry of the universe. The universe is dissymmetrical because, if the bodies constituting the solar system, each moving in its accustomed way, were placed in front of a mirror, the image in the mirror could not be superimposed on the reality. The sun's light moves dissymmetrically. A ray of light never falls continuously in a straight line on the leaf in which vegetable life is busy creating organic matter. Terrestrial magnetism, and magnetic and electrical polarity, are probably resultants of dissymmetrical forces and movements. Life is dominated by dissymmetrical actions of various kinds, whose nature we divine to be cosmic and all-embracing. I even feel that all living species are fundamentally, in their internal structure and their outward form, functions of cosmic dissymmetry."

These were the views which caused him, at Strasbourg, to expose solutions of various chemicals to the influence of powerful magnets which he had had made for the purpose, in the hope of affecting the structure of the crystals. He failed completely, just as he did later at Arbois, using a flattened solenoid with a current running through it.

The experiments he carried out at Lille in 1854, when he was appointed Dean of the Faculty there, were considerably bolder. He attempted to influence the growth of plants, from germination to death, by reversing the normal direction of the sunlight falling upon them, for which purpose he used a heliostat moved by clockwork (a mirror following the apparent course of the sun round the earth). His objective, he explained, was to find out whether "in this artificial world, in which the sun rose in the west and set in the east, the active substances of the vegetable kingdom would assume forms opposite to those they display in nature".

It is not surprising that Biot, with his realism and long experience, did his best to dissuade Pasteur from this vain undertaking. What hope was there of attaining the desired result in so short a time, when the hereditary characteristics of the plants used in the experiment had been developed and stablised in the course of hundreds of millions of years?

Duclaux, who seems to have been almost the only scientific man to encourage Pasteur in his search for the origins of molecular dissymmetry, saw the position quite clearly and could not refrain from writing as follows:

"If, in a living cell, we are to introduce immediate principles which are the direct opposite of those existing in it, we must act upon it just when it is most susceptible to influence; we must modify the cell while it is at the germinal stage, just coming into being. But the cell has received from its ancestors a definite heredity in the form of one or more active substances whose presence is enough to make it resist certain influences, and which impose a certain direction on its development. This cell contains the principles not only of what it is, but of what it is to become, and this initial force governs and steers the new forces appearing day by day in its immediate ambience. If only spontaneous generation were possible! If only we could make a living cell emerge from inert mineral matter, how easy it would be to direct its development in one way or another; to introduce dissymmetry into its structure and thus into its vital processes!"

4

Towards Micro-biology

PASTEUR was interested in everything. The range of his activities makes an overwhelming spectacle: he did so much and was passionately interested in all of it. After his appointment as Dean of the newly created Faculty at Lille he willingly responded to an appeal from M. Bigo, the father of one of his students, who, in 1856, had suffered severe setbacks in the distillation of alcohol from sugar-beet.

René Vallery-Radot considers that Pasteur's compliance sprang from his desire to be useful both to industry and to the Faculty. No doubt this was partly the case. The minister who had caused him to be appointed had, indeed, taken it upon himself to offer certain advice: "M. Pasteur must be continually on his guard not to be carried away by his passion for pure science, and to remember that academic teaching, while preserving the purity of scientific ideals, must also, if it is to produce useful results and extend its beneficent influence, take every opportunity of applying itself to the real needs of the country."

It is true that Pasteur was always deeply respectful towards authority; he worshipped the established order. He aspired to be a model public servant; and a model citizen, paterfamilias and husband; in short, a model character all round, one to whom no public blame could ever attach. But his instant readiness to concern himself with M. Bigo's refractory sugar-beet was surely caused by something more than a conscientious wish to save a manufacturer from ruin.

We must remember the circumstances of the time. There were no laboratories; none, at least, to compare with the elaborate organisations of today. Systematic scientific research really began with Pasteur, not before. Always, and especially in his early career, he had literally to beg for whatever meagre financial support he could get, and often paid for his equipment and materials out of his own pocket. But in an industrial setting most of these things were supplied free. It is true that when he was helping M. Bigo at Lille he had nothing but a primitive microscope and an ordinary coke stove; but he did have abundant scope for studying fermentation phenomena— the very subject towards which his work on tartaric acid had been carrying him.

It will be recalled that when Pasteur began his research on tartrates and paratartrates he had had to separate the crystals of racemic acid by hand. This laborious procedure had been improved by his pupil, Gernez, who succeeded in separating the two kinds of crystal by adding a single crystal, dextro- or laevo-rotatory as the case might be, to a supersaturated solution of paratartaric acid; this sometimes resulted in a selective crystallisation starting from the corresponding molecules, the molecule being the kernel round which any crystal is formed.

The next step was Pasteur's observation of the fact that whenever the two acids were mixed with potash, soda, ammonia, lime, or any kind of alcohol or ether—in other words, any compound which was symmetrical, non-hemihedral and therefore inactive with respect to polarised light—the acids and the compounds respectively derived from them always retained their identity of properties: there were as many left-handed as right-handed crystals and the whole was optically inactive.

But if the solution was exposed to the action of dissymmetrical substances, such as quinine, albumen, sugar or strychnine, the result was otherwise: "If combination takes place", wrote Pasteur, "the two resulting compounds are as different from one another as the most sharply differentiated isomers: crystalline form, specific gravity, amount of water of crystallisation, resistance or lack of it to heat—everything is different. Having seen the two tartaric acids form such dissimilar compounds merely because of their respective rotatory characteristics, I had grounds for hoping that this very dissimilarity would point the way to a chemical means of dissociating the two components of paratartaric acid."

For a long time the search was unsuccessful; then, using the two bases which were isomeric with quinine and cinchonine, he reached his goal:

"I prepare paratartrate of cinchonicine by neutralizing the base; then, by adding as much acid again as was required for neutralisation, I cause crystallisation, and the first crystals consist of perfectly pure laevo-rotatory cinchonicine tartrate. All the dextro-rotatory tartrate remains in the liquid, being more soluble. Finally it too crystallises and is easily distinguished by eye, since its crystalline form is different from that of the other."

But what caused this differentation? That was what he set about discovering in 1857. He noticed one day that a tartrate solution which he had prepared had deteriorated, apparently because the temperature of the surrounding air was higher than usual. It was visibly "fermenting"; patches of "mould" could be seen in the cloudy liquid.

The study of fermentations had already been occupying him for about a year. His rough notes for a course of lectures he delivered in the early part of 1857 include the significant words: "*What does fermentation consist of; mysterious character of the phenomenon; a word on lactic acid.*"

Fermentation had never been properly explained, though its effects had been known from remote antiquity. Very ancient documents exist which mention alcoholic drinks and give details of their making—the gas given off, the froth which builds up on the surface of the liquor as it "works", and so on. In 1682 Becher had shown that there were two kinds of fermentation, alcoholic and acetic, and that the former took place only when sugary substances were present. But nothing was known of the causes of fermentation.

Leeuwenhoeck, using the first microscope, had examined brewer's yeast and found a spherical micro-organism. But when in 1935 Cagniard-Latour in France, and Kutznig and Schwann in Germany, tried to establish a connection between these organisms and fermentation they were blocked by the authority of Berzelius and Liebig, both of whom followed Lavoisier in upholding a strictly chemical theory.

Berzelius, who was sure catalysis was the explanation, dismissed what had been seen by Cagniard-Latour, Kutznig and Schwann as "an immediate principle of vegetable species, a principle which was precipitated while the beer was fermenting and which, during precipitation, presented an appearance not unlike the simplest forms of vegetable life". But, Berzelius declared, "form alone does not constitute life".

Liebig's explanation was subtler: "The fermenting agent is an unstable organic substance which decomposes and, as it breaks down into its constituent elements, agitates the molecules of the fermentiscible liquor; it is the 'dead part' of the yeast, the part which has lived and is in process of disintegrating, which acts on the sugar."

Pasteur had too penetrating a mind to be satisfied by either of these explanations. He exposed the solution of inactive tartaric acid to the "mould" he had found in his preparation, and observed that the dextro-rotatory form was easily affected, whereas the other remained unchanged.

"The liquid," he wrote, "is found to have a laevo-rotatory power which gradually increases and reaches a maximum. Fermentation then ceases; no dextro-rotatory acid is left in the liquor. The latter, after being evaporated and replaced by an equal volume of alcohol, at once produces a beautiful crystallisation of laevo-rotatory ammonium tartrate."

In the opinion of Professor Dubos, this experiment was "the first link in the chain of reasoning which was to lead Pasteur to the study of fermentations and that of contagious diseases". Its immediate importance to him was that he regarded it as confirming his ideas about the influence of dissymmetry in vital processes. On this aspect he wrote:

"Two distinct things should be noted: as in every fermentation properly so called, there is a substance which undergoes chemical transformation and, correlatively, something is developed which has all the appearances of a mycodermic organism. Furthermore (and this is particularly pertinent) the yeast which causes the dextro-rotatory salt to ferment leaves the laevo-rotatory salt unchanged, despite the complete identity of the physical and chemical properties of the two tartrates of ammonium whenever they are subjected to non-dissymmetrical influences. Here, then, we have an example of the molecular dissymmetry which is characteristic of organic substances, entering into a physiological phenomenon, and doing so, moreover, as a modifier of chemical affinities. Thus the influence of molecular dissymmetry enters for the first time into physiological thinking and research; molecular dissymmetry, that great characteristic which perhaps affords the only line of demarcation we can draw today between the chemistry of dead nature and that of living nature."

However, the question of fermentation had attracted his attention strongly enough for him to follow Biot's advice and continue studying it, laying aside, provisionally, the problem of the molecular dissymmetry of organic matter.

HOW FERMENTATIONS TAKE PLACE

Let us glance at the process of fermentation in the light of present-day knowledge. Pasteur rightly said that fermentation cannot take place without the help of micro-organisms. But their presence is necessary only because, and in so far as, they are capable of secreting certain catalysts; these and these alone —the enzymes—are responsible for fermentation.

Enzymes are biological catalysts or "biocatalysts". Catalysts are substances which accelerate, and in some cases initiate, chemical reactions in other substances. They are all subject to the law of catalysis, which is: (a) a catalyst does not affect the nature of the products resulting from the reaction, which in principle could have taken place without it, though much more slowly, and (b) the catalyst is not affected by the reaction, but emerges unchanged from it.

Why do catalysts work like this? No one yet knows. We can describe the process but not account for it.

In inorganic chemistry, catalysts may be elements, such as platinum, or compounds. In organic chemistry (including biochemistry, the study of the chemical composition and functioning of animal and plant tissue), catalysts (the enzymes) are always compounds. Some of them are complex, with a high molecular weight.

Yeast does not cause fermentation; this is done by the soluble ferments (enzymes) produced by the microscopic unicellular organisms of which yeast consists. Berzelius, Liebig, Wöhler, and the main body of nineteenth-century academic scientific opinion, were therefore right in maintaining that fermentation of all kinds was essentially chemical, but Pasteur's retort to this statement was righter still: "In the natural setting, fermentations are impossible in the absence of a mycodermic growth."*

The question was settled by Büchner in 1897: by breaking up yeast and squeezing it he extracted a juice which contained no cells or cell-fragments, and found that this juice transformed glucose into alcohol and carbon dioxide. Pasteur would have had nothing to say against this, for, as Metchnikoff wrote, "he was in no way opposed to the theory that the action of organic ferments depends ultimately on inorganic substances".

THE PROBLEM OF FERMENTATIONS

In the "pre-Pasteurian" period the word "fermentation" was applied rather loosely to any change in organic matter which resulted in the production of alcoholic or acid substances. The work of Pasteur caused a distinction to be drawn between (a) *alcoholic fermentation*—the production of alcohol as part of the manufacture of such liquors as wine, beer and cider; (b) *acetic*

---

* *Mycoderma*: the fungous "skin" formed on the surface of a fermenting liquid; or the genus of fungi producing this. (*Tr.*)

fermentation—the transformation of wine, cider or any other alcoholic liquor into vinegar; and (*c*) *lactic fermentation*—in which the sugars contained in milk turn into acids (as when milk goes sour).

In the field of fermentation and putrefaction (which appeared to differ from fermentation only in the nauseous smell accompanying its later stages), Pasteur seems to have begun his researches by studying alcoholic fermentation. This was in 1855, but his first paper, addressed to the Lille Société des Sciences in 1857, was on lactic fermentation.

Experimenting at the factory of the industrialist Bigo, in an attempt to find out why some fermentations went wrong while others did not, he first distinguished with the naked eye what he provisionally classed as "bad" and "good" fermentations. Under the microscope, the latter were found to contain only round globules of yeast, whereas the former contained short, rod-like organisms as well as globules. The faultier the fermentation, the higher was the preponderance of rods over globules.

From the manufacturing point of view, the problem was a practical one, that of preventing the rod-shaped organisms from appearing; this could be achieved by using pure yeast, instead of the dirty, impure yeast which was used sometimes. But this did nothing to solve the problem of fermentation itself or that of the rods and their intrusive role. To the industrialist they were simply an obstacle to be avoided; but to the scientist they were worth studying for their own sake, not merely because of the harm they did to an industrial process.

We shall not describe the many experiments conducted by Pasteur, both in France and elsewhere (notably England, in connection with the brewing of beer). By means of these experiments he made a thorough study of fermentations of all kinds, and also found the cause of numerous defects in the manufacture and keeping of the various products concerned. He succeeded in raising both output and quality by means of *pasteurisation*, which consists of killing pathogenic organisms in vinegar, milk or fermented liquor by means of heat.

PUTREFACTION AND NATURAL CYCLES

Lavoisier had pointed the way to the study of "biological cycles": innumerable cycles involving oxygen, hydrogen, phosphorus and all the other substances necessary to life, which are made available in convenient forms by incessant, energy-producing transformations of matter. At cellular level these transformations are effected both in the organisms's internal environment and between the organism and its external environment. Life, a form of both the movement of matter and the evolution of matter, presents itself to our gaze as being first and foremost a dynamic structure, whose innumerable inter-actions bring about biological and psychological effects.

Lavoisier took as his point of departure the plant, which is autotrophic—that is, capable of changing matter from one form into another by feeding directly on inorganic substances. (The plant does this by means of photosynthesis, a process which had not been discovered in Lavoisier's time). He pointed out that plants, drawing their food from the mineral realm, serve as food for herbivorous animals which in turn are the prey of carnivores (both of these are heterotrophic—that is, dependent on organic material for their food). In effect, what Lavoisier said was that the materials of which all living things are made are ultimately derived from air, water and minerals.

And, he said, the cycle is completed by combustion, fermen-tation and putrefaction, by means of which the substances utilised by living creatures are continually returned to their source, the mineral kingdom, thus becoming available once more as food for plant life; and so the process goes on.

But by what process were organic materials reconverted into inorganic during putrefaction? Nobody had any idea; indeed, the minute organisms found in corpses and other putrescent matter were mistaken for results of putrefaction, of which they were really the cause. Lavoisier thought of putrefaction as a purely chemical process; fermentation was thought to be one too, and at the time when Pasteur attacked the problem this chemical theory was upheld by the most distinguished experts—Berzelius, Wöhler, Liebig and Berthelot.

It is true that putrefaction, like fermentation, is ultimately a matter of chemistry (of which biochemistry is only a sub-division). But it is none the less necessary to trace in detail the chain of causes and effects by which putrefaction and fermentation take place.

Pasteur, by showing that both these processes were made possible through the agency of living organisms, provided the logical link whose absence had prevented the underlying mechanism of the phenomena from being understood. We shall see later that this was only a stage in the single line of progress along which he was so patiently and impressively travelling, from experiment to experiment, from discovery to discovery.

In the words of Émile Duclaux, the Master's first successor as director of the Institut Pasteur, "the two papers on fermentation, one on alcoholic, the other on lactic fermentation, contain the whole microbial doctrine, which illuminated the mysteries both of fermentation and of infectious diseases".

We must repeat that the position taken up by Pasteur conflicts not at all with what is now known about the action of enzymes, the essential factor in all fermentation occurring naturally. "All fermentations", he wrote, "are phenomena correlative with the formation of globules, mycodermic plant-organisms, as in alcoholic fermentation properly so-called." He showed, furthermore, that each type of fermentation was caused by a different agent. While it is true to say that vital phenomena are essentially dependent on fermentations and the various chemical transformations and decompositions which fermentations cause, it is important, as Pasteur showed, to discover the biological starting-point of fermentation, which may be set in motion by micro-organisms, or the cells of animal or vegetable organisms, or their secretions.

DISCOVERY OF LIFE WITHOUT AIR

While studying the butyric fermentation which causes the production of an acid with a nauseating smell during the transformation of milk (or, strictly speaking, of the lactose in the milk), with carbon dioxide and hydrogen being given off at the same time, Pasteur came upon a creature which was very different from yeast globules: it could move about at speed, and he regarded it at first as an "animalcule".

For a while the busy movements of this vibrio threw him off the track; he found it hard to believe that butyric fermentation could be caused by an organism resembling the infusoria. "I thought it necessary to prevent these tiny animals from appearing", he wrote; "I was afraid lest they feed on the vegetable ferment which I thought must be the cause of butyric fermentation, and which I was trying to discover. But eventually I was struck by the fact that all my analyses showed the same thing—namely, that this butyric acid and the infusoria always occurred together."

Today we know that butyric acid and its derivatives, which are found in various fermentations, are produced by different bacilli, one of which is *Bacillus amylobacter*. But in Pasteur's time biologists had not realised that, at the microsopic level, plant and animal life meet and interpenetrate.

"Pasteur", writes René Dubos, "was not a trained naturalist and he was working alone, without a tradition behind him and without associates with whom he could have shared his thoughts in moments of doubts or astonishment. The many brief notes which he left of his observations remind one of a child running hither and thither in a wood, dazzled by the manifestations of an unknown life which he half sees, half guesses, and delighted to discover the diversity of the Creation. The fermentation of butyric acid had astounded him by showing him how intensely motile microbial life could be. Eventually it led him to discover new and unsuspected biochemical processes, and a new realm of life."

It was in fact while he was watching under the microscope a drop of liquid undergoing butyric fermentation that a new kind of life, totally unsuspected by his predecessors, was revealed to him—*anaerobiosis*, the life of organisms or tissues in the absence of free oxygen; in other words, in the absence of air, which contains free oxygen.

He had placed the drop of liquid on a glass slide and covered it with another slide—the normal procedure before putting a preparation under the microscope. He then noticed with surprise that at the edges of the drop the "bacteridia" (as they were then called) were beginning to lose their power of movement, while those near the middle were as lively as ever. This was startling: when an infusion is examined under the microscope the micro-organisms normally move out *towards the edges* of the glass, where a little air makes its way in. But the bacteria Pasteur was watching seemed actually to avoid the air and its free oxygen; they were *anaerobic*, not *aerobic*.*

But if this was the case, how was it that anaerobic organisms were also capable of surviving and developing in the presence of air—namely, in culture-broths with a normal oxygen content? This contradiction was a challenge which had to be met. Pasteur set about making a patient, systematic study of all the existing commercial techniques of fermentation—thus, incidentally, establishing a bridge between practical and fundamental research.

AEROBIC AND ANAEROBIC LIFE

It will be convenient to abandon chronology for a moment and take a bird's-eye view of the studies to which we owe the present-day science of micro-biology. Some of these studies were conducted in Paris, in the makeshift little laboratory which Pasteur, as we have described, set up in an attic at the École Normale. But most of them arose during investigations he carried out in still more unfavourable conditions, in wine-making establishments, breweries, vinegar factories and other places where natural products were fermented on a commercial scale in a number of different ways.

Pasteur showed that microscopic unicellular animals and plants were divided into three classes:

1. *Strictly aerobic*—requiring atmospheric oxygen for their metabolism.

---

* Both these words, now part of the fundamental vocabulary of zoology, were coined by Pasteur.

2. *Strictly anaerobic*—i.e. organisms which are found only in oxygen-free environments and are killed by exposure to oxygen.

3. *Facultative anaerobia*—a mixed class which includes the yeasts.

Yeasts are unicellular fungi, mostly belonging to the Ascomycetes, which split sugars into alcohol and carbon dioxide. Pasteur showed that in a highly aerated environment (a very shallow layer of sugary liquid containing a culture of yeast cells) yeast is aerobic. It breathes—that is to say it burns the sugar by making oxygen atoms combine with the carbon atoms of the sugar, with the result that water (H_2O) is formed and carbon dioxide (CO_2^-) is given off.* Each sugar molecule, consisting of carbon, hydrogen and oxygen atoms, is completely broken down.

What happens in an anaerobic environment (such as the interior of a large quantity of liquid which completely fills its container) is rather different. The sugar is incompletely broken down, yielding carbon dioxide and alcohol (the keystone of whose chemical structure is OH). In other words, fermentation occurs; away from air, the decomposition of the sugar into alcohol and carbon dioxide liberates energy which is used by the yeast. This energy corresponds to that liberated when yeast lives aerobically.

"Yeast", said Pasteur in substance, "has, therefore, two modes of life: in one, it develops very rapidly by consuming large quantities of oxygen, as the moulds and infusoria, for example, also do; in the other, it obtains the necessary oxygen by decomposing sugar. Other simple forms of plant life, which resemble yeast but do not act as agents of fermentation, cannot do this."

The butyric vibrio, on the other hand, lived only by acting as a fermentation-agent: it was strictly anaerobic. If it was exposed to oxygen its metabolism slowed down and finally stopped. Pasteur realised that if these and other anaerobic organisms were capable of surviving in a culture-broth exposed to the air, the reason must be that other microscopic germs,

---

* What actually takes place is a whole chain of oxidation-reduction reactions.

capable of consuming the oxygen dissolved in the liquid, formed a protective skin over the surface. On the basis of limited observations, he also became convinced that similar phenomena occur during putrefaction, and that the decomposition of proteins—and in general of all organic waste products—results from the action of specific germs which acquire the energy for sustaining their existence by breaking down organic matter into inorganic.

BACTERIA IN NATURE

Today, we know that the cycles of nature depend on mechanisms and interactions far more complex than those envisaged by Lavoisier. It is still possible to say, schematically, that the biological cycle starts with the plant kingdom. But where would plants get their nitrogen without the help of certain bacteria which have the power of fixing atmospheric nitrogen and making it available to plants in a form they can assimilate?

Plants, in fact, cannot absorb nitrogen directly either from decaying matter or in the gaseous form (the nitrogen in the air).* Bacteria are therefore indispensable to them, just as they themselves are to herbivores and the latter are to carnivores. But the dead bodies of animals of all kinds, from unicels upwards, and their excreta, and decaying vegetable matter, are needed by bacteria (very few species of which are capable of fixing gaseous nitrogen); otherwise bacteria could not do their job of "revictualling" the plant kingdom.

Among the innumerable bacteria which play a part in the chemistry of nature one of the most important is *micrococcus ureae*, which transforms the urea in urine into ammonium carbonate. Acting in association with the bacteria which fix atmospheric nitrogen it forms nitrogen compounds. The compounds of ammonia found in soil (and in particular those arising from putrid anaerobic fermentation) are taken up by bacteria and turned into nitrous salts, which then converted by other bacteria into nitrates.

* A recent theory, highly revolutionary and strongly contested, that of Professor Kervan, attempts to show that living matter is capable of effecting transmutations.

The sulphur which plays a part in many metabolic cycles comes from the chemical breaking-down of organic matter which has first been decomposed in stagnant water. There are bacteria which accumulate sulphur in their cell-tissues; this is subsequently transformed into sulphuric acid, which leads to the formation of sulphates. As most people know, coal consists of fossilised vegetation. Dead vegetation was first macerated in water and then transformed into carbon by bacterial fermentation.

Many pages, indeed many volumes, would be needed to describe even the known bacteria and their functions in the process of nature; and there are still many species which have not yet been identified. Putting the matter briefly, there are bacteria which are indispensable to life because they return to the inorganic state everything of which living organisms can make no further use; and bacteria which are harmful to life, pathogenic bacteria which attack living organisms; and finally, a few rare species of bacteria which seem to be the only autotrophic entities existing at the present stage of evolution, drawing all they need from inorganic material alone.

DEATH AS A NECESSITY OF EVOLUTION

With the possible exception of the last-named class of bacteria, which may be the distant descendants of a primitive world in which life was not derived from antecedent life, since as yet there was no life—but this line of thought is hedged about with reservations—it is plain to see that life, which at the present stage of evolution is born exclusively from life, has death as its inescapable corollary.

So Claude Bernard's famous saying, "Life is death", is not mere paradox or nonsense. Bitter and terrible though the thought may be, we human individuals have to resign ourselves to the fact that without death life would be impossible on the cosmic scale. We are only an incident in the existence of the human species, just as the human species is only an incident in the evolution of life on earth, and as earthly life itself is probably only an incident in the infinity of space-time.

If we were to postulate arbitrarily that death could be abolished, we should be showing not only a disordered imagination but also a complete lack of realism. For to abolish death would be to pass sentence on all organic matter: it would mean arresting, completely and irreversibly, the very life-process we had thought to protect.

BACTERIA AND VIRUSES

Pathogenic bacteria, which are capable of killing their victims, have a part to play in the scheme of things; they are no more "useless" than the bacteria of putrefaction. This, needless to say, does not mean that the victims have no defence; they have, and this defence is part of the scheme of things too. It is a matter of observation that living things have a variety of reactions with which to resist microbial attacks. Bacteriophages set about devouring the microbes; a life-and-death struggle takes place between defenders and attackers. If the latter prevail the invaded victim dies—and this applies not only to man but to the whole of the animal and vegetable kingdoms, including bacteria.

Viruses, which are still smaller than bacteria and differ from them by being unable to reproduce except in an organic environment, are capable of attacking bacteria. So are some other organisms, both animal and vegetable: notably amoebae, infusoria and, of course, moulds. (Hence Fleming's discovery of penicillin, the first antibiotic; *Penicillium*, from which the drug was originally prepared, is a mould.)

Bacteria are considerably smaller than the cells of the yeasts and moulds; they vary in size, according to species, from a few tenths of a micron to several microns.* Their shapes are simple: spheres (cocci, micrococci), straight rods (bacilli), wavy or corkscrew forms (vibrios, spirillae, spirochetae). Some bacteria possess flagella or cilia whose lashing or quivering action enables them to move about at speed.

The ease and rapidity with which bacteria absorb their food is remarkable, and is paralleled by their astonishing power of

* A micron is one-thousandth of a millimetre.

reproduction. In fact, if care is taken to provide the optimum culture medium, the interval between division of a cell and that of the resulting cells is only twenty or thirty minutes. Thus if a cell is duplicated in half an hour there will be four instead of one at the end of an hour; sixteen in two hours; sixty-four in three hours; and so on. If this was kept up the number of the original cells' descendants at the end of twenty-four hours would be more than 100 million millions, or 10^{14}.

In the next twenty-four hours this number of bacteria would increase to the square of 10^{14}, or 100 million millions times 100 million millions. Even if we set the size of a single unicel as low as 1 cubic micron, the total volume of the bacteria would be some 10 cubic kilometres. It would take less than three days for the progeny* of one unicel to equal the volume of the earth.

Of course bacteria cannot in fact proliferate like this because their food-supply is limited. Moreover, it has been found that bacterial activity is accompanied by the formation of deleterious substances: acids, such as the lactic acid formed in the fermentation of sugars; and bases, such as the ammonia produced by the putrefaction of proteins, etc.

The susceptibility of different species of bacteria to these substances varies a great deal. A substance which blocks the development of one species sometimes provides the food required by another. Thus the balance between one natural cycle and another is maintained.

THE SPONTANEOUS GENERATION PROBLEM

Pasteur did not discover bacteria and the other kingdoms of the "infinitely small". It was some two centuries since the microscope had first made it possible to observe the multitudinous life swarming in decaying organic matter, but the creatures observed were mistakenly assumed to be the effect, not the cause, of putrefaction; they were thought to appear as a result of the disintegration of matter, not the other way round. Buffon in particular had worked out a theory of imputrescible,

* Strictly speaking it is wrong to refer to the "progeny" of a unicellular organism. The organism reproduces by splitting into two, each of which is half of the "parent".

immortal "organic molecules"—on the lines of the indestructible chemical molecules which were then thought to exist—composed of indivisible atoms. The constituents of life were still thought to be radically different from those of mineral substances. A metaphysical entity, the "breath of life", was held to be necessary to animate life's materials, and the dualistic conception of Descartes (soul and body) was so firmly established as to seem impregnable.

Today, however, everything points to the underlying unity of the enormously varied phenomena which nature brings before our wondering eyes, and we are at last coming to understand that no psychological event can take place without the existence of an organic substratum which is in continual contact with the events of its own environment; a substratum which is itself composed of particles in a state of perpetual movement and interchange. These particles, let us note by the way, do not (as was believed until not long ago) exist from eternity to eternity. They represent the concentration in the form of mass, at a given point in space-time, of a primordial energy about which we know nothing whatsoever except that it "is".

All the appearances seem to show that energy/matter possesses *potentially* the power of self-organisation into more and more complex structures—"complexified and complexifying", in the apt phrase of Teilhard de Chardin. But this complexification, in which the new qualities unknown to inorganic matter—biological and psychological existence—are *immanent*, did not arise spontaneously. The study of *fossils* found in biological strata which can be dated with reasonable precision confronts us with the *slow evolution* of living matter, passing from simple forms to higher ones; though this *overall* picture of gradual evolution does not exclude the possibility of quantic (i.e. discrete) "jumps"—of which larval processes are a familiar example in the present epoch of evolutionary development.

In Pasteur's time, that is to say at the juncture when he resolutely embarked on the study of the possibility or otherwise of spontaneous generation—*in the express hope of proving that life could be generated by inert matter*, since all his experience pointed to an underlying similarity in all the forms of matter, living or lifeless—there was, of course, no one who still believed that spontaneous generation affected the higher forms of life.

This had been believed once. Diodorus Siculus, in the first century before our era, asserted that the mud of the Nile, when "sufficiently warmed", brought forth animals "of enormous size". Ambroise Paré declared that "toads are borne of the moisture of rocks and stones"; Van Helmont, that "mice can be produced by a woman's dirty shift". But all such fantasies had long since been outgrown. Even Buffon's ideas on the subject had been discarded—he had maintained that infusoria and other "lower creatures" (including earthworms and the larvae of flies, and hence the flies themselves) could make their appearance without any pre-existing germ. But notwithstanding the conscientious efforts of Redi, Swammerdam, Leeuwenhoeck and the Abbé Spallanzani to explode the myth, the most advanced scientific circles still clung to the possibility of spontaneous generation in the world of the "infinitely small": moulds, yeasts and *"bactéridies"* (as some micro-organisms were called).

PASTEUR AND MATERIALISM

To Pasteur, his defeat of the partisans of spontaneous generation or heterogenesis was in no sense a philosophical undertaking. "Religions, philosophies, atheism, materialism or its opposite—none of these is relevant to the matter," he declared to an excited audience at the Sorbonne. "I might even add that, scientifically speaking, I am indifferent to them all. The question is purely one of fact. I approached it without preconceived ideas, as ready to admit, should experience compel me to do so, that spontaneous generation existed, as I am now persuaded that those who believe in it have blindfolded themselves. . . . Science should never seek to foresee the philosophical consequences of its investigations. . . . So much the worse for those whose doctrines or systems are at odds with the truth of the facts of nature."

It is true that more than one construction could be placed on these words. But when Pasteur affirmed, "I looked for spontaneous generation without finding it, but I do not believe it to be impossible", he was undoubtedly taking up a position identical with that of modern scientific materialists, who think of spontaneous generation not as the emergence *de novo* of an organic complex identical with one of those already known, but rather as the creation of a cellular complex capable of dynamic existence, i.e. capable of maintaining a rhythmical interchange of its constituent matter with that of its environment; of growing as a result of such interchange; and of dividing in such a way as to yield an individual identical with itself, and likewise capable of perpetuating its kind in a suitable environment.

There is obviously room for endless argument as to whether or not a complex of this kind could be said to be alive. It is certain that life is more than matter-in-movement; it is also matter-in-evolution. And whatever it may be possible to achieve in the way of spatial structuration (atomic and molecular arrangements so devised as to constitute an individual "object"), we shall always lack the *time-dimension* required for observing the evolution of the "descendants" of any such dynamic aggregate created in the laboratory.

Whenever we are thinking about the origin of life and the evolution of species we should always remember that conditions during the earlier ages of our planet were very different from those we know: the environment was a reductor, and the mephitic atmosphere enveloping the atmosphere was permeable to the ultra-violet radiation of the sun. Life arose from the action of the sun's rays on molecules of nitrogen, ammonia, methane, carbon dioxide and water vapour. Inorganic matter was re-structured into amino-acids and various other compounds allied to sugar; these new structures were capable of subsequent self-organisation in terms of new energy-reactions.

The energy-conditions favourable to the emergence of organic complexes would be lethal to life as we know it now, which in the course of its evolution has become more versatile but also frailer, more precarious. Life was anaerobic at first and gradually, following the emergence of chlorophyll, generated an atmosphere containing free oxygen; and the quantity of this oxygen (ozone, i.e. triatomic oxygen) slowly increased to form a layer which excluded ultra-violet rays. Hence the conditions under which spontaneous generation took place on the Earth, some three thousand million years ago, have never since been realised.

HOW UNICELS REPRODUCE

In the nineteenth century there was still a good deal of hesitation about the distinction between the protozoa (unicellular animals) and the protophyta (unicellular plants). Classification is in fact very difficult and in parts rather unsatisfactory (the same uncertainty also obtains here and there at higher levels in the organic kingdom). Generally speaking, unicels reproduce by fission; though some of them, including some species of bacteria, have quasi-sexual reproduction (adult cells join together, separating again after junction and mingling of their nuclei).

Unicels also reproduce by spores. This is the case in many unicellular plants, notably yeasts and moulds.

We have seen what immense reproductive powers are displayed by bacteria. So it comes as less of a surprise to realise that bacteria also show respiratory powers hundreds and even thousands of times greater than man's. In twenty-four hours a man weighing 70 kilograms [about 154 lb.] produces from 1,500 to 5,000 calories (the amount depends on his activity during the period); whereas in the same length of time 70 kilograms of bacteria would produce hundreds of thousands, or even millions, of calories. Bacteria are capable of burning, per day, an amount of organic matter equal to several times their own body weight, or even several times their body weight multiplied by ten.

Only part of the foodstuffs taken in by any organism is incorporated into the structure of that organism; the percentage of material incorporated is even less in bacteria than in higher organisms; so it looks as if the chief function of bacteria is to transform organic materials into inorganic. Micro-organisms are essentially destructive; higher organisms, essentially constructive. In both cases the result is production of energy (or, to be strictly accurate, a process in which energy is liberated).

Bacteria are hardy creatures and live in the most varied conditions. Some are found in natural thermal waters at temperatures between 80° and 85° C. [176° and 185° F.]; others have been observed alive and active at temperatures well below freezing-point.

But most bacterial species thrive best at a temperature between 20° and 40° C. [68° and 104° F.]. Many are killed by being kept at 55° C. [131° F.] for one hour, and reproduction usually ceases in the neighbourhood of freezing-point. That is why sterilisation is carried out by boiling in an autoclave (a pressure heater) or by refrigeration. But we repeat, they are hardy creatures.

It is a familiar fact that meat is prevented from going bad by being kept in a cold place. Cold slows down the vital processes of the bacteria of putrefaction, and ever since Pasteur's day it has been common knowledge that organic material, even if dead, remains unchanged in the absence of those bacteria. Frozen meat kept in cold storage will keep until, with a rise in temperature, the bacteria "wake up" and resume their work of proliferation and destruction.

Bacteria can also adopt this state of suspended animation in the absence of suitable nutriment; some species can do this for a few weeks, others for years at a time. In this state they become dehydrated and, being extremely small and light, can be carried by the wind and lodged in some new environment, there to start reproducing again if conditions are favourable.

Some bacteria can survive in a state of suspended animation at very low temperatures, even as low as – 100° C. [– 180° F.]. There is therefore a possibility that we shall one day have the opportunity of reviving "fossil" bacteria taken from ice which dates back to some relatively remote geological period.

In the laboratory it is possible by means of lyophilisation or cryodesiccation (refrigeration in a vacuum) to keep bacteria and micro-organisms alive for an indefinitely long time; their vital processes come to a complete standstill but start up again as soon as the organisms are restored to a favourable environment.

Finally, some species of bacteria reproduce by means of spores. Each spore or group of spores is enclosed in a thick, highly resistant membrane and is consequently much less vulnerable to external attack than the parent organism. These spores are killed in the steriliser only if the temperature is raised to the boiling-point of water or even considerably higher.*

Summing up, then: bacteria and spores (such as the spores of yeasts or moulds) are observed in nature to survive in a state of suspended animation in all sorts of environments besides their typical one, which may be mineral, or decaying matter, or living tissue, according to species. At any but extreme altitudes and latitudes the air, soil and water are simply teeming with these organisms—a fact which Pasteur's predecessors did not know and his contemporaries were not willing to accept.

Can we blame them? Certainly not. Logic—the kind of logic so often upset by science, because its premises are based on our sense-impressions, which are thoroughly inadequate and misleading in dealing with anything very large or very small—logic seemed to be on their side against the principles postulated by Pasteur. At the same time we are bound to regret that such men as Pouchet, by no means devoid of critical acumen and scientific ability, should have gradually and quite consciously edged their way into a sectarian position and, instead of admitting their excusable ignorance, should have basely attacked Pasteur and showered him with insults.

Pasteur was not a long-suffering character. He was an ardent

* See Dubos, *Louis Pasteur, Free Lance of Science*, pp. 180-1, for Tyndall's account of the ingeniously simple way in which he got round this difficulty. (*Tr.*)

polemicist and sometimes a clumsy one, especially when dealing with the medical profession; he had unconscious feelings of inferiority towards doctors, and this made him dogmatic and highly combative. But it is impossible to doubt his intellectual integrity and the scientific rigour of his experiments; the latter, even in his own time, ought to have been enough for any openminded observer. No true scientist is ever afraid of yielding to a convincing experimental proof. But neither Pouchet nor those who more or less blindly followed him behaved as true scientists in their controversies with Pasteur.

PASTEUR'S DUEL WITH THE SPONTANEOUS GENERATIONISTS

Pasteur made his first formal allusion to his doubts about the possibility of spontaneous generation in a note presented before the Académie des Sciences on February 14, 1859, entitled *Nouveaux faits pour servir à l'histoire de la levure lactique* [New data in connection with the study of lactic ferment]. Pouchet counterattacked immediately. Pasteur answered him, with great moderation, on February 28:

"Sir,—I have received the letter you kindly wrote to me on the occasion of the note presented in my name by M. Dumas. You honour me greatly by the attention you appear to pay to my opinion concerning spontaneous generation. My experiments in this field have been too few and, I am bound to say, their results too contradictory for me to venture to hold any opinion worth communicating to you. If, in the note in question I used the expression 'spontaneous generation', the reason was that my observation had a direct bearing on that problem and added something to our knowledge of it.

"All previous experiments on spontaneous generation have been carried out with infusions of vegetable or animal matter, or with liquids containing substances which had belonged in the first place to a living organism. Irrespective of the conditions of temperature and ebullition to which these materials may have been subjected, they all possess a constitution and properties acquired under the influence of life. In my own experimenting, on the contrary, I have seen both vegetable and animal life, and (to particularise on the latter point, which is of special interest to you) I have seen *Bacterium termo* and its different varieties, appear, sometimes in considerable quantities, in a medium composed as follows: distilled water, 100 grammes; pure candy sugar, 10 grammes; pure crystallised tartrate of ammonia, 0·2 grammes; ashes of brewer's yeast (obtained by burning in a muffle), 0·1 grammes; calcium carbonate (obtained by precipitation), from 1 to 3 grammes.

"All the above solids are crystallisable.

"After twenty-four hours at a temperature of 30° C. [86° F.], a medium composed according to the above specification becomes turbid and starts giving off bubbles of gas, and the fermentation continues during the succeeding days. By the end of a few weeks the sugar and chalk have disappeared and the liquid is full of calcium butyrate and lactate. A deposit of several decigrammes of lactic or butyric ferment has formed at the bottom of the jar, mixed with dead bacteria whose development and movements have been easy to observe microscopically during fermentation. The experiment is perfectly successful even when the jar is completely filled and the tube for receiving the gases is completely filled likewise; the reason being that there was contact with the outside air during preparation of the medium.

"But, when the liquid has been prepared, boil it for a few minutes in a retort connected by rubber tubing to a small copper pipe which is surrounded by glowing charcoal; having allowed the liquid to cool, close the end of the stem of the retort in a warmed cabinet: it can be left there for months at a temperature between 25 and 35° C. [77 and 95° F.] without showing any sign of fermentation or ferments or infusoria.

"May I urge you, sir, to proceed as I suggest? In less than quarter of an hour you will set an experiment in motion which will lead you to the conviction that, in your own recent experiments, you unwittingly introduced atmospheric air and that the conclusions you reached were not based on irreproachably accurate observation of the facts.

"I therefore think, Sir, that you are wrong, not in believing spontaneous generation to be possible—for in a matter such as this it is difficult not to have a preconceived opinion—but in positively affirming that spontaneous generation does take place.

"In the experimental sciences, one is always wrong not to be sceptical until the facts force one into a positive affirmation. But I hasten to add that when your adversaries, as a result of the experiments I have described here, assert that the air contains the germs of the organic development observable in infusions, they are going beyond the evidence provided by the experiments. They ought to confine themselves to saying that ordinary atmospheric air contains something which is a condition of life; that is, they ought to use a vague word which does not prejudice the question in its most delicate aspect. One could in fact just as well say that ordinary atmospheric air contained little sodium sulphate crystals, germs of sodium sulphate—forgive me these expressions!—because that air causes the crystallisation of a saturated solution of this salt; a property not possessed by artificially heated air!

"In my opinion, Sir, the question is wholly undecided; it is virgin territory and awaits the application of decisive proofs. What is there in the air which causes life to appear? Is it germs? Or a solid substance? Or a fluid? Or a principle of some kind, such as ozone? All this is unknown, and invites experiment.

". . . Despite the invitation you were good enough to extend to me, sir, I almost feel that I should apologise for having taken the liberty of telling you what I think on so delicate a subject, which has played so small and merely incidental a part in shaping the course of my investigations.

"Believe me, etc."

Several salient points emerge from this letter, which represents the initial clash in the engagement between Pasteur and the spontaneous generationists. The first thing we note is that Pasteur is very sure of his ground where the results of his experiments are concerned, yet takes good care not to commit himself to any definite conclusion. He refused to take a single step with the opponents of spontaneous generation down the slippery slope of *a priori* thinking. He describes the technique of his experiments in detail so that Pouchet can repeat them himself without difficulty, and is at pains to make clear that this work is ultimately only a sideline for him.

Did he really mean what he said? We may legitimately doubt it. For, as we have shown, the search for the origin of life and, in consequence, the study of the possibility or otherwise of spontaneous generation, occupied him throughout his scientific career; it was the motive underlying his research both on molecular dissymmetry and on fermentations—the inquiries which had such a fruitful sequel, the microbe theory.

The fact is that Pasteur was eager to bring the question of spontaneous generation to a definitive conclusion, but Biot advised him against making the attempt. Pasteur was not a careerist when he graduated from the École Normale, but he became one under pressure from his family and friends. No doubt they thought they were advising him for his own good, and perhaps they really were; it all depends on the point of view one takes.

So when we say that Pasteur may not have been altogether sincere when he told Pouchet, "Spontaneous generation is only of incidental interest to me", we mean that he was really as intensely interested in it as ever, but that he had surrendered to Biot's persuasion, or thought he had, in the interests of his career.

But the temptation was too strong. Our argument is supported by the facts. Pasteur, much though he respected his illustrious protector's advice, finally ignored it and threw the whole weight of his ability and reputation into the "battle of spontaneous generation".

"Gases, fluids, electricity, magnetism, ozone, things known or things occult . . . it is no use talking in these terms; there is only one thing in the air which is a condition of life, and that is the germs which it carries hither and yon"—this is how we may sum up the position he was soon to adopt.

Having adopted it, he spared no effort to prove that—*under*

D

present conditions—life could be born only from life: more precisely, that new individuals could be born only from one or two parents of the same species as themselves. Careful experimental work brought him round to the view which the opponents of spontaneous generation had adopted by hypothesis: germs were carried by the air (spores of various kinds, or bacteria in a state of suspended animation).

Naturally, Pouchet and his disciples counterattacked: "How could every cubic centimetre, every cubic millimetre, of air contain unattached eggs or spores? . . . How can the germs contained in the air possibly be numerous enough to develop in infusions of organic matter? There would have to be such a crowd of them as to form a thick fog, as dense as iron!"

This was by no means a senseless objection, and Pasteur had already raised it in his own mind before taking up his stand. Is it, after all, reasonable to assume that the air which surrounds us, and which seems so clear and limpid, contains living particles? On the other hand, are we not forgetting that this same air consists of atoms which are as solid, as regards their constituent particles, as those of a metal? What counts is not what "seems reasonable", but what is true and can be confirmed by experiment. Pasteur, indefatigably taking samples from different natural media, always found they contained microscopic spores which set up fermentation and putrefaction: ripe bunches of grapes, for example, carried *externally*, on their surfaces, the germs of the ferments which turned the juice into wine in the vintner's vats and casks. "This being so", said Pasteur, "is it not likely that during the grape harvest the rain collects large numbers of these germs and spreads them on the soil of the vineyard?"

Samples taken at depths of from 10 to 15 centimetres showed that he was right.

The decisive experiments were those made by Pasteur, but many investigators before him had tried to fathom the changes which took place in *bouillons* (broths) of organic matter. They had observed that broths kept sufficiently long at a high temperature did not subsequently turn cloudy, provided they were effectively prevented from coming into contact with the air. It was not Pasteur who introduced the hypothesis that the living germs of fermentation and putrefaction entered organic liquids from the air, it was his predecessors; but they had failed to show adequate proof. The adherents of heterogenesis regarded the air coming into contact with these liquids merely as the source of the oxygen not previously supplied "to micro-organisms in a state of latent life in dead matter". What had to be demonstrated was that the air brought not only oxygen, but something else—in other words, living germs.

Against the advice of Biot and Dumas, both of whom were afraid that their protégé might be simply wasting his time, and, still more, that he might compromise his standing by attacking a generally accepted idea, Pasteur launched an impetuous assault on the positions of which Pouchet had become the quasi-official defender. Pasteur had already obtained direct proof of the presence of germs in the air by collecting samples of the minute particles suspended in the atmosphere and examining them under the microscope. This was obviously not a complete answer to the spontaneous generation theory, but it was an important piece of evidence and provided a basis for further experiment.

There is no need to enter into the details of the innumerable trials made by Pasteur with a wide variety of media—broths, blood, urine, etc. It is enough to describe one experiment which will stand as a summary of all the rest: into swan-necked flasks, which were easy to seal, he put a sugary liquid and some extract of yeast; the mixture was then brought to the boil to kill any living organisms in it and expel the air, which was driven out by the steam escaping through the narrow aperture of the neck of the flask.

When the flasks were sterilised and practically empty of air he sealed the apertures with a blowlamp while the steam was still escaping. The liquid was then found to remain clear and unclouded for an indefinite length of time, until the tip of the swan-neck was opened by being snapped off with a pair of pliers.

As soon as this was done a hissing sound could be heard as the air rushed back into the flask. The aperture was then sealed again, and all the flasks so treated were placed in an oven at a temperature suitable to the development of any micro-organisms which had been suspended in the air entering the flasks when they were broken open.

In most cases the liquid soon turned cloudy: fermentation or putrefaction took place as a result of microbial activity. In a few cases the liquid remained clear. If, as the supporters of heterogenesis maintained, the vital activity in the liquid was due merely to the admission of air or rather of the oxygen in the air, the difference was inexplicable: the liquid in all the flasks, without exception, should have become turbid.

According to Pasteur, the fact that some flasks were "inoculated" with life, while others were not, showed that the distribution of germs in the atmosphere was uneven. Were not some parts of the globe less "contaminated" than others? It seemed likely that germs would be more numerous wherever there was abundant life and consequently an abundance of organic products to support a large and prolific population of micro-organisms—namely, in places thickly inhabited by humans or animals, or on cultivated land. Germs would be correspondingly less numerous, and perhaps even absent, wherever there was a shortage of food for micro-organisms and the temperature was unfavourable, for example above the snow-line.

So Pasteur took his sterilised flasks into different environments; to the cellars of the Paris Observatory, for example, where the air is more or less isolated from life and is virtually never changed; and to the foothills of the Alps. He broke open the flasks to admit air and then sealed them as before; he took care to hold the flasks above his head while he was working, so as to avoid contaminating them with the germs clinging to his clothes or carried on his breath. Out of twenty flasks taken up on to the Mer de Glace, the contents of only one underwent alteration.

"If all the results so far obtained by me are considered together", he wrote in a note presented before the Académie des Sciences on November 5, 1860, "they enable us, in my opinion, to state definitely that the dusts suspended in the atmosphere are the exclusive origin, the initial, indispensable condition, for the existence of life in the infusions."

And in a truly prophetic sentence he revealed the goals towards which his future research was to be directed: "What would be most desirable of all would be to carry these studies far enough to prepare the way for serious research into the origin of different diseases."

Pouchet and his disciples were meanwhile travelling in Italy, from the shores of the Mediterranean to the heights of Etna, and crossing the plains of Sicily. In their flasks the liquid, unlike that in Pasteur's, always turned cloudy. There is no reason to doubt Pouchet's good faith when he wrote, "The air is equally favourable to the genesis of life, wherever a sample of it be taken: from the laden atmosphere of our crowded cities, or from a mountain top or on the open sea, where the atmosphere is extremely pure. I maintain that from a cubic decimetre of air taken from any environment whatsoever, it is always possible to produce legions of microzoa and moulds."

Pouchet's observations were in fact highly accurate, but neither the materials nor the methods of his experiments were the same as those used by Pasteur. Whereas Pasteur employed an easily sterilisable liquid extract of yeast, Pouchet employed an infusion of hay, the germs in which were not killed by the temperature to which Pasteur subjected his flasks; this explains why the former remained clear in the presence of sterile air, while the latter became turbid. It is as well to remember that when the Academies decided in favour of Pasteur, they did so without having really understood why Pouchet had failed; and Pouchet himself did not realise that he was right in detail though wrong in general.

PASTEUR VERSUS BASTIAN

A book published in 1872—twenty years after Pasteur's victory over Pouchet—raised the whole question anew. As he read this immense work of 1,115 pages by an English doctor, Henry

Charlton Bastian, published in London and entitled *The Beginning of Life: Being Some Account of the Nature, Modes of Origin and Transformation of Lower Organisms*, Pasteur was forced to recognise how precarious his victory had been. The struggle must be renewed; he must find more substantial scientific foundations for his proof of the impossibility of spontaneous generation.

Dr. Bastian had discovered that whereas acid urine, if heated and then protected against contact with the air, remained clear and apparently sterile, it became cloudy and swarmed with living bacteria within ten hours after being neutralised by the addition of potash (which is a base). He therefore maintained that it was the acidity of the urine, not sterilisation, which had prevented bacteria from developing.

Bastian had taken care to sterilise the potash which he added to the urine to neutralise it, and as an extra precaution he had dissolved the potash in distilled water. But, says Dubos, he was "unaware of the fact that the most limpid water can carry living germs". And there was another cause of contamination: at 110° C., the temperature he thought high enough to destroy "bacterial germs", Bastian failed to destroy the spores emitted by the bacteria.

Earlier, when studying the diseases of silkworms, Pasteur had noted that bacteria go through a vegetative phase during which they have a higher resistance to heat than in the active portion of their life-cycle. By following up this observation the British physicist John Tyndall, and subsequently Ferdinand Cohn, had established the existence of "bacterial spores".

A temperature of 120° C. was required to destroy these spores, which could survive at 110° but did not become active until the acidity of the medium was neutralised by addition of an alkali. By 1880, thanks to Pasteur's efforts and the support of Tyndall, whose book, *Essays on the Floating Matter of the Air in Relation to Putrefaction and Infection*, was published a year later, the question of spontaneous generation was settled once and for all, despite Bastian's belated attack; or rather, indeed, because of it.

5

Man versus Microbe

In 1868, when he was forty-six and his powers as a creative scientist were at their height, Pasteur had a paralytic stroke which developed into hemiplegia. Continual strain, caused by overwork, brought on the attack just after his return to Paris from the country in October. On the morning of the 19th he woke up with a curious feeling of discomfort, a kind of tingling all down his left side, but paid little attention to it and embarked on his day's work as usual. But after lunching at home with his family he had to lie down on his bed, ice-cold and shivering uncontrollably. He got up again, as he had undertaken to present a note at the Académie des Sciences on behalf of an Italian colleague. After the meeting he walked home with Balard and Sainte-Claire Deville, dined at nine o'clock and went to bed.

His indisposition, which he had thought was over, now returned in an acuter form. He tried to speak, but was unable to do so. Mme. Pasteur, whose anxiety may well be imagined, immediately called in a friend, Dr. Godélier, who could only report that his illustrious patient had suffered a cerebral haemorrhage resulting in a progressive loss of the power of movement on the left side. Speech returned at intervals, however, and Pasteur, remaining perfectly lucid throughout, described his symptoms to the doctors. By Wednesday, October 21, the condition had become stable. Godélier recorded in his notes on the case: "Intelligence completely unimpaired; eager to talk about science."

Pasteur, who had calmly and clearly seen himself lying at the brink of death, was now rallying his courage; and it never deserted him. Only a few nights after the attack he dictated to his assistant, Gernez, a note which was handed in at the Académie des Sciences on October 26.

Pasteur was concerned that work on the building of a new laboratory should go on. But as soon as the news of his illness had been announced the authorities had given orders for the work to stop. A cruel blow for Pasteur, for, as M. René Vallery-Radot has written, the order really implied that Pasteur was dying.

It must be put to the credit of Napoleon III that as soon as he heard of this untimely excess of zeal he wrote to Duruy, the minister concerned: "I have been informed that, doubtless without your knowledge, the workmen building M. Pasteur's laboratory were withdrawn on the very day he fell ill. This action much distressed him, since it appeared to mean that he was not expected to recover. Please give orders for work to start again."

SILKWORM DISEASES

Pasteur recovered fairly quickly from his terrible attack, but never regained the full use of his left hand. Before his illness he had agreed, at the request of Dumas, to study *pébrine*,* a disease of silkworms which was devastating French *magnaneries* (silkworm nurseries). He now set about the task with a will.

At the time he did not even know what a silkworm looked like, but the insect world was interesting enough to fascinate him as much as the world of microbes. Henri Fabre, the famous naturalist who founded the science of entomology, records the following curious conversation between Pasteur, newly arrived from Paris, and completely ignorant of the physiology of the creature he was supposed to cure, and a silkworm-breeder who handed him a cocoon.

---

* So called because tiny specks like grains of black pepper appear in the internal tissues and on the surface of the infected silkworm.

Fabre describes with considerable humour how Pasteur very gingerly took hold of the object, tried its weight in his hand, turned it this way and that, put it close to his ear, shook it and exclaimed with surprise:

"A kind of knocking noise. . . . Is there something inside?"

"Yes, indeed!"

"What can it be?"

"The chrysalis."

"How do you mean, the chrysalis?"

"I mean the sort of mummy which the caterpillar changes into before it becomes a moth."

"And there's one of these things inside every cocoon?"

"But of course! It's to protect the chrysalis that the worm spins the cocoon."

"Ah!" was all Pasteur said. And without more ado he set to work, helped by one of his best pupils, Duclaux, who in turn had the assistance of three students from the École Normale who had travelled down with them from Paris. Later they were to be joined by Mme. Pasteur herself, who turned silkworm-breeder for the occasion.

THE STUDY OF INFECTION

The study of silkworm disease, or, rather, of two such diseases, for Pasteur investigated another parasitic malady, *flacherie*, as well as *pébrine*, occupied several years, and took him as far afield as the country round Trieste. In thus labouring to save an industry from financial disaster he increased his knowledge of the "infinitely small", and Dr. Roux hailed the publication of his results as "a veritable guide for anyone wishing to study contagious diseases". In his work on silkworms, writes M. André Georges, Pasteur "had in fact demonstrated, by devising prophylactic measures against *pébrine*, how a disease caused by a parasite is picked up by the host and transmitted from one generation to the next; while in the case of *flacherie* he had shown the action of germs in an intestinal malady and had appreciated the paramount importance of the environment".

Between 1877 and 1888 Pasteur demonstrated the existence

of half a dozen species of pathogenic microbes in humans or animals: the *septic vibrio*, found in the rotting bodies of dead animals and responsible for a high mortality from septicaemia in human beings; *staphylococcus*, first discovered in an outbreak of boils from which his pupil Duclaux suffered for some time; *streptococcus*, found in the vulvar discharge of women who had died of puerperal fever; the *bacillus of chicken* cholera and that of *swine-fever*; and *pneumococcus*, which, along with his collaborators Chamberland, Roux and Thuillier, he failed to identify correctly, confusing it with the rabies virus, but which, thanks to two of his followers, Talamon and Fraenkel, was later recognised as the cause of pneumonia.

It is imperative to know the cause of a disease, especially a disease of microbial origin, since an attempt can then be made to destroy the microbe and cure the disease without harming the patient.

It is because we do not know the real cause of cancer that none of the therapeutic methods so far devised against it is really effective. Nearly all these methods are limited to destroying the cancerous growth, by physical or chemical means.

Pasteur expressed the curious opinion that cancers might be caused by affected tissue-cells competing successfully with normal cells for the nutritive substances brought by the blood. "Naïve as these views were", writes Dubos, "they deserve respect as the first statement of the problem of the nutritional relationship between parasite and invaded host."

TOWARDS INOCULATION*

When we have identified the agent of infection we are not only in a position to combat it when it attacks the organism but also to take *preventive* action against its intruding in the first place; in other words, we can resort to inoculation.

---

* Whenever possible, in this translation the word "inoculation" will be used as the general term; "vaccination" will be reserved for inoculation against smallpox. This division is in line with common English usage, but cannot be consistently maintained, because usage itself is not consistent; for example, people who habitually use the word "vaccination" in its particular sense nevertheless use "vaccine" in its general sense. (*Tr.*)

It must be made quite clear at this point that it is only in very exceptional cases that inoculation is used to cure rabies, because the rabies virus has a very long incubation period. Inoculation is essentially a method of immunising the organism in advance against a given pathogenic agent.

Pasteur showed that it was not absolutely necessary to identify that agent in order to counteract its ravages effectively.

But this does not alter the fact that infectious agents exist. Inoculation does not apply to non-infectious diseases.

The concept of infection and contagion—that is to say, of diseases transmitted by living germs—is not due to Pasteur alone. To point out that a scientist had predecessors is not to diminish his merit. Thus, in the first century before our era, Varro and Columella put forward the hypothesis that certain diseases might be caused by the intrusion of small invisible creatures (*animalia minuta*) conveyed either in the food or in the breath.

At the time of the epidemic of syphilis which spread through Europe in the late fifteenth and early sixteenth centuries—the disease was imported by the Spanish and Portuguese along with the gold they had plundered—it became obvious enough that contact was the means by which infection took place. In the sixteenth century the Italian physician Fracastoro formulated the first clear statement that certain diseases were transmitted by a living agent (*contagium vivum*).

Very early attempts were made to draw a connection between disease and putrefaction, and between putrefaction and fermentations. In 1663 Robert Boyle wrote in his essay, *Offering Some Particulars Relating to the Pathological Part of Physick*:

"He that thoroughly understands the nature of ferments and fermentations, shall probably be much better able than he that ignores them, to give a fair account of divers *phenomena* of several diseases (as well fevers as others) which will perhaps be never thoroughly understood, without an insight into the doctrine of fermentation."

"In fact", says Dubos, "the concepts dealing with fermentation and contagious diseases followed a parallel evolution during the two centuries which followed Boyle's statement. In both cases, two opposing doctrines competed for the explanation of the observed phenomena. According to one, the primary motive force—be it of fermentation, putrefaction or disease—resided in the altered body itself, being either self-generated, or induced by some chemical force which set the process in motion. According to the other doctrine, the process was caused by an independent, living agent, foreign in nature and origin to the body undergoing the alteration, and living in it as a parasite. It is the conflict between these doctrines which gives an internal unity to the story of Pasteur's scientific life. He took an active and decisive part in all phases of the conflict, and succeeded in uniting in a single concept those aspects of microbial life that have a bearing on fermentation, putrefaction and contagion."

If we remind ourselves that Pasteur's life of research began with the study of crystallography, which led him to show the dissymmetrical character of living structures and of the substances produced by living organisms, we gain an impressive glimpse of those powers of analysis and synthesis which make of Pasteur the greatest biologist of all time.

But to resume our story. Before Pasteur's advent the idea was already gaining ground that diseases were caused by microscopic agents and were transmitted from one individual to another by those same living agents. Swann, who had recognised the living nature of yeast as early as 1837, was in close touch with Henle, the teacher of Robert Koch. Henle had expressed the opinion that "the demonstration of the causal role of a given microscopic agent in a given disease would require that the agent be found consistently in the pathological condition, that it be isolated in the pure state, and that the disease be reproduced with it alone."

Koch, not Pasteur, was the first to succeed in satisfying all these conditions, though the microbe with respect to which he achieved it had been discovered by two Frenchmen; *Bacillus anthracis*, the cause of anthrax (a disease of herbivorous animals, especially sheep, which can be transmitted from animals to humans), had been described in 1850 by Royer and Davaine.

THE ANTHRAX "BACTERIDIA"

Whatever form it takes—malign oedema, broncho-pulmonary or intestinal attack—anthrax is a dangerous disease and may prove fatal. Human beings contract it by contact with an infected animal, living or dead (the intestinal form is caused by eating infected meat, especially minced liver). Inoculation against it is now commonplace, thanks to Pasteur, and the disease is no longer the scourge it used to be.

Controversy both about priority and, subsequently, about technique in connection with anthrax was the root of the regrettable animosity which grew up between Pasteur and Koch. Let us try to re-establish historical truth by quoting Dubos: "One of Koch's experiments was of particular interest in proving the aetiological role of Davaine's rods. He had sown fragments of infected tissues into drops of serum or of aqueous humour of the rabbit, and had allowed this primitive culture to incubate until the bacilli had multiplied to large numbers; then, from this first culture, he had inoculated a new drop of serum. After repeating the process eight times he found to his great satisfaction that the last culture injected into a susceptible healthy mouse was as capable of producing anthrax as blood taken directly from an animal just dead of the disease. Despite their thoroughness and elegance, these experiments still left a loophole for those who believed that there was in the blood something besides the rods, capable of inducing anthrax. Although Koch had transferred his cultures eight times in succession, this was not sufficient to rule out the possibility that some hypothetical component of the blood had been carried over from the original drop and was responsible, instead of the bacteria, for transmitting the infection to the inoculated animal. It was this last debatable point that Pasteur's experiments were designed to settle."

When he began his work on anthrax, Robert Koch was a young doctor, aged thirty-three, whose scientific equipment consisted almost exclusively of the microscope which his wife

Emmy had given him on his twenty-eighth birthday. Pasteur, though his laboratory at the École Normale was still very simple, had more than a quarter of a century of experimental practice behind him. He set about his task in his usual way, working methodically, in successive stages. From infected animals he took specimens of blood, in which he confirmed the presence of the filiform bodies which Royer and Davaine had found free and unattached in the blood serum, among the red and white corpuscles. He injected a single drop of this blood subcutaneously into various animals, a guinea-pig, a rabbit, a sheep, a cow and a horse. The inoculated animal invariably died after one or two or at the most four days, and the whole of its blood was found to be infested with anthrax bacilli, as the drop had been.

It seemed clear enough that the "bacteridia" caused death. But it still remained to be proved that the "bacteridia" was directly responsible, and not some element accompanying it. To a pure culture in a glass flask Pasteur added a drop of infected blood. The culture at once became infected; the anthrax bacteria multiplied so fast that Pasteur exclaimed, "We could prepare pounds and pounds of them!" Everything except the microbe disappeared, and it became evident that the microbe was the initial, real and exclusive cause of the infection.

But in nature, blood is not transferred in this fashion from one animal to another. How then did *Bacillus anthracis*, unless it was produced spontaneously (and spontaneous generation was discredited by now), make its appearance in previously healthy animals?

"By ingestion of food" was Pasteur's answer—because anthrax was seen to appear suddenly in a whole flock which had previously been perfectly sound; the disease appeared to occur spontaneously in every animal in the flock. Pasteur proved that the animals infected themselves by eating infected grass. The source of the infection was the dead bodies of animals which had died of anthrax and had been buried in the fields; the microbes were carried to the surface by earthworms and ejected in the wormcasts.

THE SEPTIC VIBRIO

Several other experimenters were working on anthrax at the same time, injecting blood from animals which were said to have died of the dreaded disease into healthy animals. The latter invariably died, but in some of them, notably those tested by Paul Bert, *Bacillus anthracis* could not be detected. This seemed to invalidate Pasteur's contention. He admitted as much, but refused to admit defeat. With the help of Joubert, he resumed his patient studies of blood specimens, and observed the presence of another organism: besides the anthrax bacillus, the blood taken from anthrax victims and injected into healthy animals (which died, but apparently not from anthrax, since no anthrax bacilli were found in their bodies) also contained a sinuous transparent microbe, the *septic vibrio*. Its transparency had caused it to be overlooked.

The septic vibrio worked so fast, killing the animal in twenty-four or thirty-six hours, that the anthrax bacillus did not have time to proliferate in the blood of the victim, which was consequently killed by septicaemia instead of by anthrax. So far from the theory of microbial infection being invalidated, it was confirmed. Pasteur's work on anthrax enabled him to prepare his first vaccine; animals previously subject to the disease could now be protected.

LA MICROBIE

From now on, the study of the "infinitely small", which had so far not been given any official classification, was known to Pasteur and others as *la microbie* (in modern parlance, "microbiology").

The word "microbe" means "short life", and was used for the first time in 1878 by Sédillot in a communication to the Académie de Médecine. Microbes had previously been known as animalculae, bacteria, *bactéridies*, spirilla, etc.

Microbes were rendered visible by the invention of the microscope. It is probable that the first man privileged to see them was Leeuwenhoeck, but they did not really arouse the curiosity of scientists until Pasteur had demonstrated the part played by some of them in causing disease.

Nevertheless, as has been mentioned already, the idea that diseases might be transmitted by minute organisms had been entertained as early as the first century B.C.: malaria, for instance, was attributed to an invasion by "small invisible animals" through the mouth or nostrils. This conviction was abandoned for many hundreds of years, and was not revived until the seventeenth century. In about 1720 the English doctor Benjamin Marten maintained that tuberculosis was caused by an "animalcule", but he did not succeed in getting his opinion generally accepted.

The prevailing theory in Pasteur's time, in pathology as in fermentations, was that catalytic processes, more or less spontaneous in origin, were responsible; a chemical theory, in fact. This was the view held by the highest scientific authorities, from the German Virchow to the Frenchman Claude Bernard. The "spontaneous" theory of disease was summed up in the dictum, "Disease is in us, of us, through us".

In the light of modern knowledge we can see that this was a retrogade step from the position reached by the ancients. Fortunately, there were a number of isolated researchers who refused to be satisfied by such vague conceptions. They persisted in allowing the possibility that some pathological processes were initiated by an external cause. Everyone knew that a poison caused sickness or death. The poison might be inorganic (mercury, for example) or organic—a substance of vegetable or animal origin. This being so, why rule out the possibility that swallowing microscopic creatures might produce the same symptoms as swallowing a drop of poison or a small quantity of some vegetable juice?

The opponents of the microbial theory, and in particular the spontaneous generationists, were doubtless perfectly right in maintaining that disease was ultimately a chemical phenomenon; where they went wrong—immensely wrong—in the case of disease as in the previously cited cases of fermentations and putrefaction was in making no attempt to discover the

mechanism by which the ultimately chemical effect was produced.

It should be mentioned in passing that some diseases do
originate directly from catalytic action (at least, that is the
picture which emerges from our present knowledge of the facts)
—or, to put it more precisely, from the partial failure of a
catalytic mechanism.

Diseases arising from hormonal disequilibrium are a case in
point. Similarly, a vitamin deficiency (hormones and vitamins
are biological catalysts) is capable of causing serious disturbances in cellular metabolism, with striking external symptoms.

So we must beware of dogmatising. Psychosomatic medicine
has shown us what serious trouble can be produced by neurological disturbances, whose origin is purely psychological (or at
least appears to be). The study of hysteria, in particular, has
taught us that the hysterical subject is a histrionic performer
(an unwitting performer, it is only fair to remember) who
manufactures his illness from his own resources, and this illness
may manifest itself in a serious external form and reproduce
the most diverse symptoms or syndromes. It is probable that all
disturbances not directly caused by infection, including those
regarded as "mental", arise from a multiple origin, partly psychological, partly physiological, and that these two factors are
interwoven in a highly complex way, each acting on the other.

However, we must return to the point of view held by Pasteur
and see how he fared. His opponents were clearly defeated.
Infection could only be exogenous, and appropriate counter-
measures had to be taken; these might consist of preventing the
intrusion of pathogenic germs (Lister's antiseptic methods), or
of destroying these germs once they had entered the body and
begun multiplying (modern antibiotics are the most striking
example in this category), or, finally, of limiting or completely
inhibiting their action (preventive inoculation).

FROM VACCINES TO INOCULATIONS

One of the characteristics of life is its ability to adapt itself,
within limits, to new environmental conditions.

It has been known from very ancient times that an organism can get used to a substance which would normally be harmful to it; if the dose is increased gradually enough it can reach what would normally be lethal proportions, yet do no harm.

Mithridates, King of Pontus (123-63 B.C.), rendered himself immune to various poisons by drinking the blood of geese to which they had been administered. The inhabitants of Styria (and their horses) can take large quantities of arsenic because the soil of the region, and consequently its plant life, are abnormally rich in arsenic; a correspondingly high tolerance for arsenic is the result. Morphine addicts tolerate doses which would kill anyone whose system was not already intoxicated by the drug. Bee-keepers and snake-hunters become immunised after being stung or bitten a number of times.

It had long been realised that these empirical facts held a promising pointer to the successful treatment of disease, provided disease had an external origin. Natural immunisation and artificial inoculation have much in common.

Historically speaking, vaccination has its origin in the attempts made by various peoples to protect themselves against smallpox (variola). This disease, which has been widespread since very ancient times, at best disfigures its victims for life, and at worst kills them.

It has always levied a heavy toll in Asia, and especially among the Chinese and Siamese, both of whom are known to have made a practice of placing scabs from smallpox sufferers in the nostrils of healthy individuals; this was done as early as the ninth century.

In Persia, bath attendants used to rub liquid extracted from smallpox sores into scratches on the skins of their customers. The Circassians and Georgians protected their most beautiful girls by "pricking them in various parts of the skin" with needles infected by contact with smallpox patients.

These rough-and-ready methods, studied by the British doctor Edward Jenner in the latter part of the eighteenth century, enabled him to achieve the first *vaccination*.

The disease known as *vaccine* in French and cow-pox in

English is a pustulous rash occurring chiefly on the udders of cows. The connection between cow-pox and immunity to small-pox is very ancient; history records that in Baluchistan children with sore or scratched hands were protected against smallpox by being made to milk cows which had cow-pox.

The practice had been gradually adopted in Europe. Jenner therefore thought of trying the following experiment: he took a little vaccine virus from the hands of a young woman infected with cow-pox, and inserted it in a cut made on the arm of an eight-year-old boy. This inoculation was successful. After a number of trials, he was in a position to prove that the cow-pox virus gave protection against the smallpox virus. In other words, he showed that cow-pox from a cow could be transferred to a human being by inoculation; that it could be similarly trans-ferred from one human to another; and that patients who had cow-pox did not catch smallpox during an epidemic.

PASTEUR AND INOCULATION

"In the field of experimentation", wrote Pasteur, "chance favours only the prepared mind." It is in this sense, therefore, that we must interpret the random cause which, when he was sixty years old and semi-paralysed, directed him towards the most profitable to mankind of all the work he undertook in the whole of his astonishing career; the work which entitles him to be regarded as the virtual initiator of *immunology*.

A culture of chicken cholera, about which he had already written a note presented to the Académie de Médecine in the early part of 1880, was abandoned in the laboratory in the hurry of leaving Paris on holiday. Since they were no longer being fed, the microbes stopped reproducing. Pasteur was on the point of throwing away this culture, which seemed to be of no further interest, when he suddenly changed his mind. He injected a syringeful of the apparently weakened culture into a hen, which showed no ill effects. He subsequently treated a whole batch of hens in the same way.

Some time later he treated this batch of hens and another batch, which had not been inoculated; he injected into each individual of both batches a syringeful of fresh culture. The inoculated batch survived; the others, without exception, died.

Pasteur instantly grasped the implications of his experiment. Relating the phenomenon to Jenner's vaccination, he adopted the same term *vaccination* for this process of preventive inoculation, or *immunisation*, to the study and development of which he was to devote the remaining years of his life.

From the start he was concerned with two problems: finding the most convenient and reliable ways of attenuating the virulence of the microbial culture; and applying the method to as many different diseases as possible.

A given microbe may be virulent to one species of host but not to others. By "virulence" is meant the ability of a microbe to multiply in the tissues it invades. Virulence varies not only from one species of host to another but also with environmental changes.

Pasteur had already found that chicken cholera could be transmitted from poultry to rabbits and vice versa—that is to say, the disease was fatal to both species, although they were zoologically remote. But the guinea-pig, though so closely related to the rabbit, seldom or never died of chicken cholera. Experimentally injected into a guinea-pig, the bacillus merely caused an external abcess which healed of its own accord. But if the abcess was opened and pus from it was injected into rabbits or hens, they died.

Pasteur's experiments with anthrax played the biggest part in revealing the influence of the environment—both on the activity of microbes themselves (their pathogenic power in relation to physical or chemical changes in the environment) and on the organism's ability or otherwise to resist microbial attack. Thus, for example, anthrax bacteria ceased developing in neutral chicken *bouillon* if the *bouillon* was raised to 45° C. [113° F.]. They would continue developing at 42 or 43° C. [approx. 108 or 109° F.] but no longer produced spores, whereas at the temperature of the host's body, or at that of the soil, development, including spore-production, was normal.

Chicken cholera vaccine was easy to make: as Pasteur had

discovered by accident, it was enough to leave pure cultures of
the bacteria alone for some time, exposed to the air. They then
lost their virulence, yet had the power of conferring immunity.

THE MECHANISM OF IMMUNITY

The mechanism of immunity was unknown to Pasteur, as it
had been to Jenner and, naturally, to earlier workers. Since the
time of Metchnikov, who was one of Pasteur's most brilliant
pupils (but who had already achieved lasting distinction before
his long stay in France), a certain amount has been known
about this important question.

We have come to understand that the organism has several
different kinds of reaction to draw upon in its fight against
microbial intoxication. Before we enumerate them, we must
take a brief general glance at a typical microbial invasion. In
order to live, microbes must derive energy from their environment—that is to say, from the body of the host; as we now
know, they feed on certain cell-constituents of the host. It is
obvious enough that the development of a large microbial
population must rapidly upset the biological equilibrium of the
infected tissues, and that this in turn will affect the biological
equilibrium of the organism as a whole.

Like all living things, the microbe does not only feed, it
excretes; it transforms substances which were useful to the host-
organism into others which are useless to it. It deprives the
tissues of substances whose absence renders life difficult or
impossible to maintain; at the same time it unloads into its
environment a large and varied class of products known as
endotoxins. By depriving the tissues of enzymes it sets up
abnormal biochemical reactions; if these disturbances are not
brought under control the afflicted organism ceases to perform
its vital biochemical tasks, and the result is death.

Some bacilli, such as those of diphtheria, for instance, and
tetanus, are only moderately virulent but have an extra
capacity for harm through their power of producing poisons
known as *exotoxins*, the first of which was discovered by another
great follower of Pasteur, Émile Roux.

All the processes involved in the relationship of microbe to host are ultimately of a chemical nature, and it is by calling biochemical processes to its aid that the host defends itself.

The first of these reactions is a rise in body-heat of the affected organism: the invalid "runs a temperature". But this *hyperthermy* seems to be triggered by a *hypothermy* (low temperature), the mechanism of which is still very imperfectly known. What apparently takes place is that metabolism is at first reduced, because the invading microbes take some of the substances required for it, and then tries to make good its losses by rising to an enhanced rate.

Another reaction, which also occurs directly after the invasion, is that free phagocytes concentrate in the threatened area and, by means of the enzymes they secrete, attempt literally to digest the microbes.

Finally, much later (two or three weeks after the onset of the disease, on the average), *antibodies* make their appearance on the scene and lighten the task of the phagocytes. The latter remain important, however, throughout, since it is their job to "mop up" the invaders.

Antibodies are of various kinds; those concerned in the organism's defence against microbes can be classified as follows:

(i) Antibodies produced in response to the antigenic action of the exotoxins secreted by the microbes themselves.

(ii) Antibodies produced in response to other antigenic mechanisms: (*a*) *lysins*, which dissolve microbes; (*b*) *agglutinins*, which stop microbes from growing by sticking them together; (*c*) *opsonins*, which make the microbes easier for the phagocytes to digest.

An antigen is *any* tissue normally foreign to the tissues of the organism; the term does not cover only microbes or the toxins they secrete. The organism's response to antigens is the reason why grafts of tissue from another organism are so difficult, and usually impossible, to achieve. The organism produces an antibody which is specific to the antigen, and which combines chemically with it.

Recent research has shown the existence of another set of

defences possessed by the organism (paraspecific immunity or *autarcesis*), including, in the case of virus attacks, the production of *interferon*, a substance whose action is much quicker than that of the antibodies and which, being of low specificity, holds out immense medical possibilities.

"Interferon" is derived from *interference*; very roughly, what happens is that a virus attacking certain cells in the organism finds its path blocked by another virus. A cell becomes coated with a virus, which may be active or not, and which effectively shuts out another virus, not necessarily of the same type.

GENIUS AND LUCK

These subtle mechanisms are still far from having been elucidated, and in Pasteur's time they were completely unknown. To get his results he had to grope his way forward, step by step.

Anthrax vaccine, for example, was much more difficult to develop than chicken cholera vaccine. Vaccination against anthrax cannot be achieved by empirically injecting an anthrax culture. If the virulence of the culture exceeds a certain level the experimental injection simply acts like an ordinary microbial infection.

The serum used in smallpox vaccination is not derived from smallpox itself, but from cow-pox; it so happens that the reaction providing immunity is the same for both diseases, and that cow-pox (or horse-pox) is a benign disease in human beings. This is a matter of chance. Pasteur's vaccinations, on the other hand, and those that have been developed since his time, were the result of a long and laborious search for a means of attenuating the virulence of the microbes to the requisite degree.

It was indeed chance, or luck, which enabled Pasteur to see that certain cultures had to be "attenuated" before they could be used for immunisation. But luck would have been wasted on him if he had not been capable of profiting by it.

Chance, in one guise or another, has frequently attended the birth of discovery. Chance evidence comes to everybody; but only a genius is capable of interpreting it correctly.

Yet genius alone is not enough. Without adequate scientific training, the most intelligent individual remains incapable of interpreting the play of accidental factors; incapable, too, of experimentally reproducing some phenomenon which chance has thrown in his way, so as to ascertain whether his deductions are valid or not.

Perhaps primitive man made his first accidental discovery when he noticed that he could utter an almost infinite variety of sounds. He was then able to begin constructing language. And language has enabled mankind to hand on, from individual to individual and from generation to generation, the fruit of experiences some of which were due to chance but all of which had demanded intelligence and a great deal of hard work. . . .

6

Some Potentialities of Pasteur's Work

THERE is one very important aspect of Pasteur's achievements which might yet provide scope for research—namely, variations in the virulence of disease germs in consequence of variations in their environment. It is true that in devising certain vaccines Pasteur did make use of his own observations in this field, but he seems to have had neither the time nor the facilities for exploiting them to the full.

As an example, consider a culture of chicken cholera bacilli which has lost its virulence. Pasteur showed that such a culture was still capable of killing sparrows and other small birds. When it was transferred from one sparrow to another and so on, killing them all, it gradually regained its virulence until it was once more powerful enough to kill poultry. This is not so very astonishing; even if a culture is attenuated, it does, after all, still consist of microbes, which may normally be expected to regain their original qualities when allowed to multiply in a new medium. But how are we to account for the fact that in some cases it is possible to modify the virulence of a microbe, not only quantitatively, but qualitively as well? The pneumococcus, for instance, the cause of pneumonia—a bacillus detected for the first time by Pasteur in the saliva of a child suffering from rabies, and confused for some time with the invisible rabies virus—was found to be highly virulent to rabbits but hardly at all to guinea-pigs. It could be rendered less virulent to rabbits and more so to guinea-pigs by inoculating newborn guinea-pigs with it.

Pasteur was convinced that this had an important bearing on the epidemiology of certain infectious diseases. He expressed the conjecture that an epidemic might be started by a renewed outburst of virulence in the micro-organisms responsible for the disease; perhaps even, on occasion, by an ability possessed by the microbes or their spores to acquire virulence for a different animal species as a result of some factor in the external or internal environment.

He wrote as follows:

"Virulence appears in a new light which cannot but be alarming to humanity; unless nature, in her evolution down the ages (an evolution which, as we now know, has been going on for millions, nay, hundreds of millions of years), has finally exhausted all the possibilities of producing virulent or contagious diseases—which does not seem very likely. What is a microscopic organism which is inoffensive to man or a given species of animal? It is an organism which is incapable of developing in our bodies, or those of the animal species in question. But there is no guarantee that if it gained a foothold in one of the myriad other species of the Creation, it would not invade it and make it ill. Its virulence, increased by passing successively through individuals of that species, might become great enough to be dangerous to some large animal species, such as man or certain of the domestic animals. It is possible to create new virulences and contagions by this method. I am much inclined to believe that this is the way in which syphilis, plague, yellow fever and so on have made their appearance in the course of the centuries, and that a phenomenon of the same sort is responsible for the great epidemics of various kinds which occur from time to time."

Since the Porton incident, that is to say since the death of a British research scientist, Dr. George Bacon, who was studying the possibilities of bacteriological warfare at a mysterious establishment in Wiltshire, it has been known that there are human beings, men of science,* who are exploiting this aspect

* Not, unfortunately, only in Britain!

of Pasteur's theories, not for the protection of the human race,
but for its destruction.

INHERITED AND ENVIRONMENTAL FACTORS

Though the spread of a microbial infection obeys a general law,
it does it differently in different individuals. Some are carried
off in record time; others catch the disease, but recover from it.
A few seem to be immune, to some diseases if not at all.

Of course these differences can be attributed to disparities
in the functioning of the organism's defences, disparities
brought about by environmental variations, such as vitamin
deficiencies and the like.

But there are other, deeper-lying causes, probably of an
hereditary nature, which affect both individuals and races.
Tuberculosis, for instance, seems to pass some people by,
whereas others have a predisposition to it; and the black races,
even in their own countries, are more susceptible to it than the
white.

Cancer, or more precisely the numerous forms of cancer, may
be caused, as is now coming more and more widely to be
thought, by a virus. Nevertheless, cancerous cells inoculated
experimentally into volunteer subjects (prisoners in the Ohio
State Penitentiary) caused no growth to occur in any of these
cases, and some researchers have suggested that there may be
a specific anti-cancerous substance secreted by the body (pro-
perdine of Pillemer), and that this is deficient or has been
destroyed (by the introduction of carcinogenic substances into
the organism, or by ionising radiation) in those who develop
this dreaded disease.

Charles Nicolle has referred in general terms to "chemical
relationships existing between certain constituents of bacteria
and the substances composing the humours and cells of the
living organism". "Unfortunately", he added, "we know
nothing about these connections, which appear to be like the
relationship between a key and the lock that it opens."

It is well known that pathogenic bacteria can be present in
an organism without causing trouble so long as there is no

significant change in their environment; the pneumococcus is a case in point. When Pasteur discovered the existence of the septic vibrio, which causes septicaemia, he showed that it was abundantly found in nature and was normally present in the gut of various animals (non-telluric germs) and in soil (telluric germs).

The septic vibrio is anaerobic. In the alimentary canal it is protected from the toxic effects of air by myriads of aerobic, non-pathogenic bacteria which continuously consume the oxygen they need for survival; the environment is nevertheless not anaerobic, and though the septic vibrio is not destroyed it does not proliferate in normal tissues, just as it cannot invade a clean wound in contact with the air. In what conditions, then, is it capable of developing? Only, said Pasteur, when the access of the air to the tissues is limited or when a large number of associated bacteria (as in the case of heavy infection by pathogenic bacteria) completely exhausts the oxygen present; an anaerobic environment is then created and the septic vibrio develops freely, secreting its toxins.*

MICRO-ORGANISMS AND THE "STRUGGLE FOR EXISTENCE"

Disease is an example of the notion of reciprocal interactions which is essential for our understanding for the mechanisms of life, and Pasteur was the first to regard disease as a form of the "struggle for existence", a contest between micro-organisms and the tissues they attempt to invade. For instance, anthrax bacilli compete with the red corpuscles of the blood, according to Pasteur, for the oxygen needed by them both, and the corpuscles are partially asphyxiated in consequence. In his view the dark colour of blood and tissues affected by anthrax was a clear sign of oxygen-deficiency. He showed that by secreting soluble poisons microbes could cause certain morbid symptoms and lead to the death of the infected tissues and

* Septicaemias, which consist essentially of a poisoning of the blood by toxins secreted by microbes, can also be caused by aerobic germs: staphylococcus, streptococcus, pneumococcus, meningococcus, gonococcus, *Bacillus coli.*

consequently to that of the organisms to which those tissues were indispensable. He filtered blood taken from an animal which had anthrax, in order to clear it of bacilli, and noticed that when he added some of the filtrate to a sample of normal blood the immediate result was an agglutination of the red corpuscles, exactly as in the disease itself. This was the first time anyone had succeeded in showing that physiological disturbances could be caused by the *products* of microbial life, even in the absence of the microbes which had manufactured those products.

But the most conclusive of all Pasteur's experiments concerning the possibility or otherwise of microbial infestation was the one which enabled him to beat one of his stubbornest opponents with the latter's own weapons.

This opponent was Dr. Colin, professor at the Veterinary School at Alfort. At meetings of the Académie de Médecine he had acquired a certain notoriety by consistently opposing Pasteur's view on spontaneous generation, the role of micro-organisms in putrefaction, and the aetiology of anthrax. When Pasteur asserted that birds, especially hens, could not contract anthrax, Colin, without proof, said they could. Pasteur, who never missed a chance of controversy, at once sent Colin a culture of the microbe and invited Colin to bring him in exchange a hen which had died of the disease.

This was in March, 1878.

"At the end of the week", Pasteur wrote, "I saw M. Colin coming to my laboratory, and even before I shook hands with him, I said, 'Why, you have not brought me that diseased hen!' . . . 'Trust me,' answered M. Colin, 'you shall have it next week.' . . . I left on holiday; on my return, and at the first meeting of the Académie which I attended, I went to M. Colin and said, 'Well where is my dying hen?' 'I have only just begun experimenting again,' said M. Colin; 'in a few days I shall bring you a hen suffering from anthrax.' . . . Days and weeks went by, with fresh insistence on my part and new promises from M. Colin. One day, about two months ago, M. Colin acknowledged that he had been mistaken, and that it was impossible to give anthrax to a hen. 'Well, my dear colleague,' I told him, 'I will show you that it *is* possible to give anthrax to hens; I shall myself, one day, bring to you at Alfort a hen which will die of the disease.'"

What was the origin of the contradiction? Here we see the full brilliance of Pasteur's genius. "Why," he had asked himself, "are not hens susceptible to anthrax, like mammals? Perhaps because their temperature is higher." (The normal internal temperature of a hen is in fact sometimes as high as $42°$ C.) He immediately inoculated some hens with a virulent anthrax culture and placed them in cold water, with the natural result that, after their bodies' initial defensive reaction to the cold had been overcome, their temperatures fell. All the hens subjected to this somewhat barbarous treatment died the next day, and their blood, spleen, lungs and liver were found to be filled with bacilli.

To show that chilling was not the cause of death, Pasteur had placed an uninoculated hen in the same bath for the same length of time; it did not die, neither did an inoculated hen which was not chilled. On the other hand a hen which had been inoculated and chilled, but withdrawn sufficiently soon from the icy bath, developed some signs of the disease but finally recovered. Pasteur noted that in no case did the temperature of the hens fall below $38°$ C., and that this comparatively slight reduction was enough to render them almost as receptive to infection as rabbits or guinea-pigs.

Professor Dubos points out that the problem of the influence of body-temperature on the susceptibility of hens to the anthrax bacillus is undoubtedly more complex than Pasteur thought: "True enough, the cooling of chickens by immersion in cold water brought their body-temperature down to a level compatible with the growth of the anthrax bacillus, but at the same time it probably interfered with the performance of normal physiological mechanisms, thus increasing the susceptibility of the animals to infection. The results, nevertheless, were of interest as being the first experimental demonstration that environmental factors influence the course of infection, and that the presence in the body of a pathogenic agent is not necessarily synonymous with disease."

We may add that these experiments also seem to explain why some illnesses start from a chill; why, in a given species, some individuals and racial groups are more susceptible than others to a given microbe, if they are moved from their usual habitat to a different environment; why fever is the first reaction in the struggle of the organism against microbial infection; and more besides.

7

Research on Rabies

PASTEUR is chiefly known to the public at large for having discovered the antirabic vaccine. But this was only one episode in his working life. In spite of its terrifying character rabies cannot be compared, in its statistical effect on mankind, with the great epidemic diseases and with other, less spectacular types of infection for which Pasteur devised remedies.

Except in Central America, where the vampire bat is one of the chiroptera which dares to attack large mammals (including man), and is therefore able to infect them with the rabic virus (of which it is sometimes a carrier), rabies is usually contracted following a bite from a so-called "mad" dog or wolf.

At the time, wolves still haunted the countryside of France and other European countries. No doubt partly because of this, rabid dogs were much commoner than now. Nevertheless the contribution of rabies to the extremely high mortality of the period was practically negligible. In France the official annual figure for deaths from rabies was about 100. The example of Germany and Australia had shown that strict police regulations, providing for the slaughter of all stray dogs suspected of rabies and the imposition of quarantine in the case of other dogs with any sign of the disease, were sufficient to protect the population.

Why did Pasteur turn his attention to rabies? It has been claimed that a childhood experience made a deep impression on him: a rabid wolf had rushed through the streets of Arbois, biting animals and men alike as it went. Horrified, Pasteur had watched the cauterisation of several such victims—no other cure then existed—at a smithy not far from his home. He is said to have remembered the patients' yells of pain at the touch of the red-hot iron, and the sickening smell of burnt flesh. He had seen eight of the sufferers die, after terrible agonies. Strangely* all of them were afflicted with hydrophobia; the slightest effort to drink, or the sight of a liquid or of anything shiny which recalled the shimmer of water, or even the memory of drinking, gave the patient such a distressing sensation of choking and suffocation that he automatically stopped taking all liquids, ejected his own saliva and behaved more and more as if out of his mind. For several years the people of the district lived in dread lest another rabid wolf appear, and Pasteur is supposed to have been specially affected by the general feeling.

Very possibly he was. But rabies and its manifestations were sufficiently mysterious in themselves for the study of them to attract his insatiably curious mind, nobody hitherto having discovered an effective treatment.†

Except for the terrifying symptoms of the last stage, rabies is a disease which runs its course very quietly. The incubation-period varies: fourteen days for bites on the face, several months if a limb is bitten; the average is thirty to sixty days. During this latent phase the wounds cicatrise and it is only after decicatrisation that the typical sensations occur—burning, tingling, stabbing or shooting pains, etc.

The pathogenic agent responsible for rabies is still invisible in our own day: it is a filterable virus, the "rabic virus", which shows a preference for the central nervous system—the spinal marrow, medulla oblongata and brain. This accounts for the symptoms mentioned above, whose characteristics point clearly to a neurological origin.

* We say "strangely" because a rabid dog or wolf drinks copiously of whatever liquid it can find.

† In some cases paralysis is one of the symptoms. Since Pasteur lived under the shadow of paralysis, would not this fact in itself have been enough to interest him in rabies?

It is the protracted incubation-period which makes it possible to cure rabies with a vaccine. In most diseases a vaccine is a preventive measure: it causes the organism to build up a reserve of antibodies which are specific to a given microbe.

It should be noted in passing that a vaccine and a serum are not the same thing. It is true that serum therapy is a treatment based on the principle of immunity, but, whereas vaccine therapy confers a more or less permanent *active immunity*, serum therapy consists of giving the patient injections of serum* from another subject (human or animal as the case may be) which has undergone infection by the same microbe, with the result that the serum contains antibodies which prevent that microbe with the result that the serum contains antibodies which prevent that microbe from proliferating. This is called *passive immunity*. Serum therapy is quick-acting, but the effect lasts only for as long as the serum, and the antibodies it contains, remain in the organism; unless the latter produces its own antibodies the treatment has to be repeated.

ENTIRELY NEW METHODS

Antirabic vaccine, then, works like an ordinary vaccine; consisting of germs with attenuated virulence, it causes the production of antibodies which come on to the scene before the virus has had time to reach its active stage, and which successfully combat the virus.

Of course this is an over-simplified account of what happens. In practice, Pasteur's experiments on rabies demanded the creation of entirely new methods, and before he could produce his vaccine he had to solve a number of highly complex problems, which we shall not describe here.

We must, however, outline the principal stages of his research. From the start he was faced with the fact that no microbe to which rabies could be attributed was ever found in the bodies of animals which had died of that disease. Today, we know why: rabies is caused by a virus, and Pasteur was not in a position to suspect that such things existed; the means for

* Serum is the non-coagulable part of the blood.

detecting them had not been developed. Despite our present-day technical achievements this is still the case for numerous viruses, that of rabies included.

Viruses are extremely small and will pass through porcelain filters impenetrable to bacteria (hence the term "filterable viruses", which is still in use). Consequently they can be examined only with the electron microscope, which had not been invented when Pasteur was conducting his research. It is now known that the anatomy and physiology of viruses are markedly different from those of bacteria.

Unlike bacteria, which will live in any suitable nutritive medium, viruses need a living environment: they are inevitably parasitic on cells. Though they are not exactly "naked genes" their enzymatic equipment is very slight and in some cases non-existent; that is why they can proliferate only in living tissue.

In assuming that rabies always started from an infection, Pasteur was relying on intuition, but was not without strong arguments in favour of his contention. Everyone admitted, as a matter of observation, that the disease was communicated by a bite. It was therefore likely that the germ was conveyed by the animal's saliva.

But whereabouts in the body did the germ develop before it reached the saliva?

"As one watches the successive stages of rabies", according to Roux, "what seems to be going on is the development of the virus in the nervous system of the rabid animal. Anxiety, and the furious condition induced by excitation of the grey cortex of the brain, are followed by alteration of the voice and difficulty in swallowing. The medulla oblongata and the nerves arising from it must therefore have been affected; finally the spinal cord itself is invaded, and the drama ends in paralysis."

The idea that rabies goes for the nervous centres is a very old one. Pasteur took a small quantity of cerebral tissues from the brains of dogs which had died of rabies, and injected it sub-cutaneously into dogs and rabbits; they contracted rabies. He was then able to write: "The rabic virus is found not only in

the saliva but also in the brain, with a degree of virulence at
least equal to that which it possesses in the saliva of rabid
animals."

The next step was to discover a method of vaccination. There
is no need to describe the material difficulties encountered by
Pasteur and his collaborators, and the controversies directed
against them from various quarters, and the opposition of the
inhabitants of Meudon to the erection of kennels for dogs both
rabid and healthy. Pasteur won in the end, and the kennels
were put up near Saint-Cloud, in the park of the château of
Villeneuve-l'Étang.

Despite his infirmity Pasteur exerted himself unsparingly.
On one occasion he collected saliva directly from the mouth of
a rabid bulldog, with two courageous employees holding it.
He knew that preventive vaccination of all existing dogs was
out of the question (there were 100,000 in Paris, 2,500,000 in
the country as a whole; how many were there in Europe, and
how many in the world?). But the very long incubation-period
of rabies held out some hope that *therapeutic vaccination* might
be possible, and this was in fact the *tour de force* which he
achieved.

Fragments of tissue from the spinal cord of a dog that had
died of rabies, which were rightly assumed to contain the virus
in a virulent state, were injected while still fresh into the dura
mater of a trepanned rabbit; the disease appeared after an
average incubation-period of a fortnight. The rabbit died and
some of its spinal marrow was injected into another rabbit;
incubation was shorter each time the process was repeated,
until, after the twenty-fifth transfer, it was only a week. It
remained at that level during the next twenty-five transfers and
then diminished by a further day, remained thereafter remarkably stable until the ninetieth transfer.

At that point Pasteur stopped. The experiments had gone
on for three years, without any interruption in the sets of
rabbits used.

"There is therefore nothing simpler", wrote Pasteur, "than to
have constantly available, over considerable periods of time, a

rabic virus of perfect purity, always identical in its characteristics or nearly so. . . . The spinal cords of these rabbits are
rabid throughout their length, with the same virulence at
every point."

The problem of attenuation had been solved by taking
fragments of infected spinal marrow and suspending them in dry
air; the activity of the virus became less and less and at the
end of two weeks there was no further virulence. The method
of vaccination was arrived at empirically; it consisted of
making a series of injections, beginning with non-virulent
extracts made from marrow which had been subjected to
prolonged desiccation, and then using extracts which were
progressively fresher and more virulent.

But this means, healthy animal subjects were rendered
immune to rabies, even if the virus was subsequently injected
directly into the brain, after trepanning. Dogs treated after
being bitten by rabid dogs—that is to say, after being infected
naturally, never contracted rabies. What was the mechanism
of this immunity? No one knew. Antibodies had not been
discovered. "The months went by", says Vallery-Radot,
"without its becoming possible to explain how antirabic
vaccination worked, any more than it was possible to explain
how Jenner's smallpox vaccination worked."

What was certain was that the vaccine immunised animals
against rabies. And it was no less certain that, because of the
long incubation period, the vaccine could be used successfully
even when infection had already taken place.

THE ANTIRABIC VACCINE AND HUMAN PATIENTS

"The thought of injecting into man rabic virus, even though
attenuated, was terrifiying", writes Professor Dubos. "Furthermore, the procedure went counter to one of the medical concepts of the time, namely, that one could not deal with virus
once it had become established within the animal body. It was
bound, therefore, to stir up great and justified opposition from
conservative physicians. In fact, the opposition to the application of the rabies treatment to human beings did not come only

from the medical world at large, but even from Pasteur's own laboratory. Roux, in particular, felt that the method had not been sufficiently tested to justify the risk of human trial. . . ."

This was the state of affairs when, on the morning of Monday, July 6, 1885, Joseph Meister arrived in Paris with his mother. Nine-year-old Joseph had been knocked down by a mad dog two days earlier, in the village in Alsace where he lived, and savagely bitten in various parts of the body, including his face and hands. He had been picked up covered in his own blood and the froth from the animal's mouth. Fortunately, Dr. Weber, who had treated him by the only method available—namely cauterisation with carbolic acid—had been an interested reader of such of Pasteur's notes on the antirabic vaccine as had already come out in the specialised publications which printed papers communicated to the Académie des Sciences and the Académie de Médecine. He took the momentous decision to send Mme. Meister and her son straight to Pasteur.

Taken by surprise, consumed by anxiety, wondering whether he dared intervene, Pasteur first asked two of his fellow-members of the Académie de Médecine, Professor Vulpian and Dr. Grancher, to examine the child and make a diagnosis. Their verdict was uncompromising: Joseph Meister would certainly develop rabies. Pasteur therefore had to choose: was he to take action—which, at this early stage in the study of the disease, might mean killing the patient, or should he abstain, thus condemning the boy to death or, at the least, to total paralysis? In the latter event, he himself would be exempt from criticism; and his friends and assistants advised him to play safe.

If he decided to act, he could only bring harm to himself: if he failed, his enemies would give him no credit for humane intentions—on the contrary, they would accuse him of presumption; and if he succeeded they would be able to say that nothing showed the case to have been desperate—the patient might have survived in any case. They would probably bandy phrases about the irresponsibility of an experimenter who had no hesitation in using a "human guinea-pig" if he saw a chance of new glory for himself—carefully overlooking the fact that

Pasteur was already destined for such glory, since the antirabic vaccine, if not yet fully developed for human use, was not far from being so.

Pasteur was therefore jeopardising his position by accepting what must be regarded as one of the most daring gambles in the history of medicine. He deliberately chose the harder course.

On July 8, at eight in the evening, in Pasteur's presence, the first injection was given—half a Pravaz syringeful of non-virulent extract from the spinal cord of a rabbit which had died of rabies.

Little Joseph Meister was nervous of the first few injections; thereafter he got used to them and put up with them boldly and even gaily. The bites healed and no longer gave him any pain. Every night, before he went to sleep, he saw Pasteur lean over his bed; he stretched out his arms and kissed him.

For Pasteur ("dear Monsieur Pasteur", as Joseph called him) the time of anxiety was by no means over. "Insomnia, which usually spares men of action", notes René Vallery-Radot, "is merciless to men of thought; it grips them in its coils. During those slow, dark hours of the night when everything is out of proportion and sagacity is the plaything of phantoms, Pasteur, away from his laboratory, forgetting the accumulation of experiments which assured him of success, imagined that the child was dying."

As we know, Joseph Meister did not die.* Fifteen months after his cure, 2,490 people—men, women and children—had been given exactly the same treatment, after being bitten by rabid dogs or wolves. There were ten failures, but these were due to help being sought too late. Of the successes, how many can be accounted real cures? Not necessarily all, both because the disease is communicated only by deep bites and because rabies is not invariably fatal. This much must be conceded. So must the fact that the vaccination in general, and antirabic vaccination in particular, does very occasionally misfire.

* Pasteur's account of the Meister case will be found in the Selected Writings at the end of this book.

Professor Dubos comments: "It is probably true that the antirabies teatment may bring about paralytic symptoms in a few cases, although these are not necessarily due to the active virus present in the vaccine. Fortunately, these accidents are extremely rare and it is almost certain therefore that the accusations directed against Pasteur on this score were unjustified. There was perhaps more ground for the attacks aimed at the efficy of the treatment."

Statistics can indeed be made to say almost anything, and the figures given by Pasteur are not always convincing. We borrow a further quotation from Dubos, a follower of the Pasteur tradition of whose authority and sincerity there can be no doubt: "Even granted that the antirabies treatment had saved the lives of a few human beings, this would have been only meagre return for so much effort, and for so many animals sacrificed on the altar of man's welfare. The same result could have been obtained, at much lower cost, by the muzzling of dogs and by the training of their owners to keep them under control. It is on much broader issues that Pasteur's achievements must be judged. He had demonstrated the possibility of investigating by rigorous techniques the infectious diseases caused by invisible, non-cultivable viruses; he had shown that their pathogenic potentialities could be modified by various laboratory artifices; he had established beyond doubt that a solid immunity could be brought about without endangering the life or health of the vaccinated animals. Thanks to the rabies epic, men were to the immunised against yellow fever and several other widespread virus diseases; even more important, immunisation had become recognised as a general law of nature. Its importance for the welfare of man and animals is today commonplace, but only the future will reveal its full significance in the realm of human economy."

Pasteur tried, though without success, to explain the mechanism of immunity. Having observed that many microbes apparently produced substances which proved inimical to them, he wrote: "It may be that the life of the microbe, instead of subtracting or destroying certain substances in the bodies of animals, actually adds substances which impede its own further development."

If he had been granted time to investigate this hypothesis experimentally he would have seen that it was not tenable, but that substances with the property of inhibiting the development of the infectious agent nevertheless are produced in the infected body. He would have discovered, as did his brilliant pupil, Émile Roux, that it is not the microbes, but the tissues they attack, which produce substances capable of halting the invasion.

8

Pasteur's Last Years

In 1887 Pasteur suffered a further paralytic attack, and there-after was unable to take any personal part in experimentation. Soon, he even had to relinquish his post as permanent secretary of the Académie des Sciences. The slightest exertion was becoming too much for him. He was overcome with sorrow at the thought that he might die without contributing anything further to science. His inability to work was made all the harder to bear by the fact that his intellect remained perfectly lucid almost to the end. His only consolation was that the Institut Pasteur, founded with the help of subscriptions from all over the world, was a growing entity. He was able to open it in person on November 14, 1888, but the speech he had dictated to Mme. Pasteur had to be read by their son.

If, in that speech, he spoke of "a scientist's patriotic duty", as he had so often done before, he also said, *"Science has no country"*. He wanted to make it clear that if at one time he had let himself be carried away by the pomps and vanities surrounding a monarch, he had subsequently done some salutary re-thinking on the matter.

This new profession of faith was expressed in the closing sentences of his address to Carnot, the President of the Republic:

"The opposite laws seem to be in conflict at the present time: a law of blood and death, ever devising new methods of war and

compelling the peoples of the world to hold themselves in constant readiness for the battlefield, and a law of peace and work
and deliverance, whose only thought is to liberate man from
the ills besetting him. The first thinks only of conquest by
violence; the second, of the relief of suffering. The second
values a single human life more than all military victories; the
first would sacrifice hundreds of thousands of lives to the
ambition of one man."

This was a total condemnation of war—war of whatever
kind and for whatever reason. Pasteur at this stage of his life,
at the height of his glory but free of ambition, knowing that his
body was incapable of anything but further suffering, had
reconciled and unified Pasteur the man with Pasteur the scientist. His mind, liberated from human contingencies but still in
full possession of its faculties, was drawing up the last will and
testament of a man pre-eminent throughout the world, and
throughout history, for his work on behalf of all mankind; a
man whose message now was, "We do not ask a sufferer, What
is your country, what is your religion? We say to him, You are
suffering and that is enough for me: you are mine and I will
help you."

This was the man who, on his last public appearance—on
December 27, 1892, at the celebration of his scientific jubilee at
the Sorbonne—reiterated his message for all to hear:

"You bring me the deepest joy that can be felt by a man
whose invincible belief it is that science and peace will triumph
over ignorance and war, that nations will unite, not to destroy,
but to build, and that the future will belong to those who will
have done most for suffering humanity."

To his disciples, who were carrying out his task in the great
Institut he had founded, he gave the following practical advice:

"That enthusiasm which has possessed you from the outset,
my dear collaborators—keep it, but let strict verification be its
travelling-companion. Never put forward an opinion which
cannot be simply and decisively proved. Make a cult of the
critical spirit. By itself it can neither awaken ideas nor spur the

mind to great things. Without it, everything is frail and precarious. Invariably, it has the last word. What I am asking of you, and what you in your turn will ask of the pupils whose minds you will shape, is the hardest thing of all to a man of original bent. To believe one has discovered an important scientific fact, to long to announce it, and yet to restrain oneself for days, weeks, sometimes even years; to strive to disprove one's own experiments; to publish one's discovery only after exhausting every alternative possibility—yes, the task is a hard one. But when, after long endeavour, certainty is reached, the reward is one of the keenest joys of which the human soul is capable."

On the occasion of his jubilee he even offered an apology to his colleagues for having "sometimes disturbed the calm of the Academies"—adding, however, that "it was simply that I wanted to defend the cause of truth".

Pasteur was indeed "a man of truth", as Jean Rostand has called him. And, as Paul Langevin has said, "The quest for truth really was the passion of his life." He himself would not have allowed himself to be described as a man possessed of every perfection.

In October, 1894, he stayed for the last time in the old family house at Arbois, and then returned to his flat in the Pasteur Institute, where his disciples came to him with their confidences: Yersin, who had just discovered the plague bacillus, Roux, who was engaged in inventing the treatment of diphtheria, Metchnikoff, who was observing phagocytosis, and others, such as Calmette and Nicolle, whose names are famous in the annals of the Pasteur tradition. "One must work," was the *leitmotiv* of his conversations with them. He refused to talk about himself and his physical condition, which, after an attack of uraemia in November, had deteriorated so far that those about him no longer dared hope for his recovery. He himself was under no illusions; he knew death had advanced upon him once again and was about to win the game.

On January 1, 1895, Alexandre Dumas brought him a bouquet of flowers. With exuberant gaiety, reminiscent of his father's, he did his best to amuse the sick man by describing the

"vibrios with human faces" which he observed in society. At
the end of April, when many people had already forgotten
about him, he received a party of students from the École
Normale who were celebrating the centenary of the school, and
to everyone's surprise he had himself carried into Roux's
laboratory, where he spent a long time examining the plague
bacillus under the microscope. "Ah, what a lot there still is to
do!" was his only comment. This was the last time he ever
looked at micro-organisms. On June 13 he left the Institute in
the Rue Dutot and settled in the annexe at Villeneuve-l'Étang,
where the administration of anti-diphtheria serum was being
organised. His paralysis was getting worse and speech was more
and more of an effort. All he could do now was to listen while
Mme. Pasteur read to him, under the trees in the spacious park.

On September 27, just as she was offering him a cup of milk,
his face filled with an expression of unspeakable resignation.
"I can't," he murmured. Those were his last words. His head
fell back on the pillow; the laboured breathing of the death-
struggle soon gave way to the serenity of sleep. Intermittently
and unconsciously, during the next twenty-four hours, he
resumed the struggle, but most of the time he lay motionless,
with closed eyes. On September 28, a little before five o'clock,
the life of Louis Pasteur came to an end.

Selected Writings

le phénomène rotatoire, ou sa cause probablement la
dissymétrie de l'arrangement moléculaire
phénomène si général parmi les produits
de l'organisme, est lié directement au rôle
physiologique de ces produits, et que cette
qualité de la matière peut avoir son intervention
directe dans les forces vitales.

Cela posé voici le fait sur lequel je veux
appeler votre attention. Dans un des mémoires
que je prépare j'établirai un mode de fermentation
de l'acide tartrique qui le transforme en acide
succinique et divers autres acides volatils.

Or cette fermentation n'a pas lieu ~~dans les~~ dans
les mêmes conditions avec l'acide tartrique
gauche, et avec l'acide paratartrique il y a
dédoublement en acide droit qui se
fermente et acide gauche qui ~~reste~~ intact.

C'est le fait ~~tout nouveau~~ que j'ai désiré
vous faire connaître dès qu'il a été ~~pour~~
~~moi~~ hors de doute, persuadé qu'il vous
intéresserait ~~on ne peut gueres~~ beaucoup.

Some of Pasteur's Notes and Reflections

IF I had to live my life over again, I would try always to remember that admirable precept of Bossuet: "The greatest disorder of the mind is to believe that things are so because we wish them to be so."

*   *   *

I know of no remedies for cancer. I have nothing but preconceived ideas on that subject, and God knows how often, in such difficult problems, *a priori* views turn out to be wrong when put to the test of practice.

*   *   *

I should like to be younger, so as to devote myself with new ardour to the study of new diseases.

*   *   *

Nearly all great artists have been great of heart.

*   *   *

I have, and mean always to have, no political bias. All I want to be is a citizen, a worker devoted to my country.

*   *   *

Where dogs are concerned, the best thing to do is not to become involved. It is very painful to part with a dog you love, but quite painless never to start loving one. So don't keep a dog.

> (Answer to a question put to him during his work on rabies.)

*   *   *

In the sciences, some people have convictions, others have

only opinions. Conviction presupposes proof; opinions are usually based on supposition.

* * *

When we feel our strength failing our only consolation is to tell ourselves that we can help our successors to do more than we have done, and do it better, by marching with their eyes on the distant horizons which we were able only to glimpse.

* * *

Never make any assertion which cannot be simply and decisively proved.

* * *

To believe one has discovered an important scientific fact, to long to announce it, and yet to restrain oneself for days, weeks, sometimes even years; to strive to disprove one's own experiments; to publish one's discovery only after exhausting every alternative possibility—yes, the task is a hard one. But when after long endeavour, certainty is reached, the reward is one of the keenest joys of which the human soul is capable.

* * *

Base minds win popular favour because they are undistinguished by any form of superiority.

* * *

Two opposite laws seem to be in conflict at the present time: a law of blood and death, ever devising new methods of war and compelling the peoples of the world to hold themselves in constant readiness for the battlefield, and a law of peace and work and deliverance, whose only thought is to liberate man from the ills besetting him. The first thinks only of conquest by violence; the second, of the relief of suffering. The second values a single human life more than all military victories; the first would sacrifice hundreds of thousands of lives to the ambition of one man.

* * *

There does not exist a category of sciences to which we can

give the name of "applied sciences". *There are science and the applications of science,* the latter related to the former as the fruit to the tree which bore it.

* * *

I feel the sufferings of animals keenly enough never to have taken up hunting or shooting. The cry of an injured lark would stab me to the heart. But when we are to probe the mysteries of life and acquire new truth, the sovereignty of the end in view carries all before it.

(In answer to an anti-vivisectionist protest.)

* * *

To claim to bring religion into science is the sign of a false reasoner. But the man who tries to bring science into religion is worse, because he is bound to a greater respect for scientific method.

* * *

Science should never concern itself with the philosophical consequences of its investigations.

* * *

The cultivation of the sciences in their highest form is perhaps even more necessary to the moral state of a nation than to its material prosperity.

* * *

Where are the true sources of human dignity, of liberty and of modern democracy, if not in the idea of the infinite, an idea before which all men are equal?

* * *

Often some remark from a man who is completely un-educated, but who does his work well, is infinitely precious.

* * *

Any scientist who allows himself to be lured by the prospect of industrial applications automatically ceases to be the servant of pure science; he clutters up his life and thinking with preoccupations which paralyse his faculty for discovery.

*   *   *

If a man has committed himself to the pursuit of theoretical science he should never, for the sake of his peace of mind and the success of his investigations, let himself be lured into the practical applications of science.

*   *   *

The loftiest conceptions, the most legitimate speculations, acquire a body and a soul only when they have been confirmed by observation and experiment. If laboratories were suppressed the physical sciences would become the image of barrenness and death. They would be limited and impotent, mere teaching-material; they would cease to be sciences of the future and of progress.

*   *   *

Enthusiasm is the god within, who leads to everything. In the field of experimentation, chance favours only the prepared mind.

*   *   *

Keep your enthusiasm, but let strict verification be its travelling-companion.

*   *   *

Make a cult of the critical spirit. By itself it can neither awaken ideas nor spur the mind to great things. Without it, everything is frail and precarious. Invariably, it has the last word.

*   *   *

Whenever I approach a child his presence inspires two feelings in me: affection for what he is now, and respect for what he may one day become.

Lessons on Dissymmetry

(*Extracts*)

IF we consider material objects, of whatever kind, from the point of view of their shapes and the repetition of their identical parts, we quickly recognise that they fall into two classes, characterised as follows: those which, when held before a mirror, give an image which can be superimposed on the original; and those whose image, though it faithfully reproduces every detail of the original, nevertheless cannot be superimposed upon it. A straight staircase, a stalk with distichous leaves, a cube, the human body, are examples of the first category. A spiral staircase, a stalk with spirally arranged leaves, a screw, a hand, an irregular tetrahedron, are forms belonging to the second category. The latter have no plane of symmetry.

We also know that a chemical compound is an aggregate of identical molecules, each of the molecules being built up of elementary atoms distributed according to laws which determine the nature, shape and arrangement of the molecules. The basic individual entity, in any such substance, is the chemical molecule, which is a group of atoms—not a random group, a huddle, but a closely determined structure. Such is the constitution which all physicists agree in attributing to matter.

This being the case, it would have been most astonishing if nature, whose effects are so various and whose laws permit the existence of so many different bodies and substances, did not display molecules exemplifying respectively both of the two categories into which all material objects can be classified. In other words, it would have been very extraordinary if chemical substances, whether natural or artificial, did not display forms which in some cases could be superimposed on their mirror-images, and in others not.

Things are in fact as we should expect; all chemical substances, without exception, fall into one or the other of two classes: those with superimposable images, and those with non-superimposable images.

*   *   *

The tartaric acid molecule is dissymmetrical, and its dissymmetry is of the non-superimposable type. The molecule of laevo-rotatory tartaric acid consists of a group of atoms which is the exact inverse of the group forming the molecule of dextro-rotatory tartaric acid. And by what signs do we recognise the existence of molecular dissymmetry? On the one hand, by non-superimposable hemihedry; on the other, and more especially, by the rotatory optical property when the substance is in solution.

This much having been established, if we examine all chemical substances, whether encountered in nature or in the laboratory, we shall easily ascertain that many of them possess both this species of hemihedry and the molecular optical property, and that the rest possess neither of these characteristics.

*   *   *

All substances produced artificially in the laboratory, and all mineral species, have a superimposable image. On the other hand, most organic natural substances (I could say all, if I confined myself to those playing an essential part in plant and animal life), are dissymmetrical, and their dissymmetry is of the kind whose image is not superimposable.

*   *   *

If the mysterious influence which is responsible for the dissymmetry of natural substances were to change its direction, the constituent parts of all living things would assume an inverse dissymmetry. Perhaps we should find ourselves confronted by a new world. Who can say what the structure of living creatures would be like if cellulose, instead of being right-handed as it is now, became left-handed, and if blood-albumen, which is left-handed, became right-handed? These are mysteries which will call for immense efforts of investigation in the future, and which already demand the most serious scientific consideration.

*　　　*　　　*

Is it not at once necessary and sufficient to postulate that a dissymmetrical force presides over the formation of immediate principles* in any plant organism?

What is the source of these dissymmetrical actions, which may arise from some cosmic influence; does that source lie in light, or electricity, or magnetism, or heat? Is it related to the movement of the earth, or to the electric currents by which physicists account for the earth's magnetic poles? We are not as yet in a position to put forward any conjecture whatsoever concerning the problem. But I believe we are compelled to conclude that dissymmetrical forces are concerned in the construction of all organic products; forces which seem to be absent or without effect in chemical reactions induced in the laboratory, either because these reactions take place so abruptly or through some other, unknown cause.

(From Pasteur, *Œuvres*, Vol. I, published by Masson et Cie, Paris.)

---

* Immediate principles: the ultimate constituents (whether solid, liquid or gaseous) into which a given plant or animal can be resolved from the anatomical point of view, i.e. without chemical analysis. (*Tr.*)

Correspondence[*]

SHORTAGE OF RESOURCES IN LABORATORIES

. . . DURING the current year I have been devoting, and am daily still devoting, to my laboratory the money awarded to me last February by the Académie des Sciences for the Grand Prix de Physiologie.

There is no need for me to describe in detail the inconveniences of this situation. I would only be repeating what I had the honour of communicating to Your Excellency in my letter of December 13, 1859. I pointed out at that time that it was impossible for me to keep my annual expenditure lower than 1,500 francs.

The purpose of the letter which I now have the honour of addressing to you is to renew, and slightly to augment, the request I submitted on that occasion.

(From a letter to the Minister
of Education, August 26, 1860.)

To the Minister of State, August 13, 1861

Sir,—The decree of November 24, 1860, having placed in your hands the allocations devoted by the State Budget to the encouragement of the Sciences, I have the honour to address to Your Excellency a request for indemnification to the amount of 3,000 francs, to cover the cost of the experiments on fermentations which I have been conducting for several years, and which are far from terminated.

* Published by Éditions Flammarion, Paris.

Four years ago the Minister of Education was good enough to grant me a separate laboratory at the École Normale, the expenses of which have so far been met as follows: (1) by a grant of 2,500 francs from the Académie des Sciences in 1858; (2) by the Prix de Physiologie Expérimentale awarded to me by the Académie in 1859; (3) from my own resources.

During the current year, as a result of the papers on fermentations which I had the honour of submitting to the judgement of the Académie, the Chemistry Section, represented by MM. Dumas and Chevreul, proposed to use part of the unexpended endowment of the Prix Montoyon to make me a grant of 3,000 francs for the continuation of my researches, the latest results of which I had made known. This proposal was approved by the Académie. But when the Administrative Committee was about to execute the decision it found that the funds allocated under the budget of the Académie were already committed, and that so far from there being a surplus there was actually a deficit.

It is in the light of the above facts, Sir—facts which give you a guarantee of the importance of the work for whose completion I have the honour of inviting your enlightened interest—that I make bold to submit my request, and to hope that it will be favourably received.

I have the honour to be
Your Excellency's humble servant.

. . . In the course of several pieces of research to which I have lately been devoting my time, I have been struck by the large number of investigations which remain to be made into fermentation in general and the fermentation of grape-juice in particular. If you read carefully the few pages I am sending to you you will see how many new ideas arise in the mind, for instance concerning the germ question. Consequently I intend to go to the Jura every year, a month earlier than usual, so as to be able to pursue on the spot, in the middle of a vine-growing district, some of the many investigations of which grape musts and sugary musts in general are susceptible. Even if I have to burn my furniture, like Bernard Palissy, I am determined to set myself up with a laboratory in the country this year. I cannot afford to do this on my own, and am therefore trying to build it by raising subscriptions from some of the silkworm breeders who are directly benefiting from my studies. A bold move, but practicable. I began yesterday . . .

(From a letter to the Danish brewer
Jacobsen, December 8, 1878).

To the Minister of Education

. . . Allow me to emphasise the urgency of this work [the building-work in progress at the École Normale]. The site has become so muddy as a result of the recent rains and thaws that no visitor can venture into it, and a day or two ago the mason's cart was left stuck there for the night, until an extra horse was brought the next day. . . .

(January 6, 1881.)

PASTEUR COULD BE VERY MODEST ON OCCASION*

To Ernest Legouvé, August 30, 1881

Mon cher Maître,—René has given me your kind and affectionate letter and also that of M. Alexandre Dumas, whom I have already thanked for his kindness in supporting my candidacy.

It is just as I told you: with you on my side I am certain of success. I am under no illusions; M. Alexandre Dumas's vote in my favour is at least half due to the friendship between yourself and him, and it will be the same with many others. You lead the way.

What greatly pleases me in the whole matter is that my election will have had nothing to do with politics. All parties will have a hand in it. The de Broglies will be associated with the Legouvés and the Nisards. This particularly delights me.

Believe me, *mon cher Maître* . . .

* The occasion concerned in the first letter was his candidacy for the Académie Française.

To X ...

November 1, 1881.

Sir,—Mme. la baronne de Pages has asked me to write to you about the illness of Admiral Pothuau, and has expressed a desire that I should come to his help with a remedy for an illness which she suspects of being caused by some infectious parasitic agent.

But, sir, Mme. de Pages has much too high an opinion of my merits. She is doubtless unaware that I am not a doctor and that I am in no position to accede to her very charitable wish.

I am, etc.

LETTER TO SAINTE-BEUVE*

Dear Sir and illustrious colleague,—I am most favourably inclined towards M. Charles Robin because his work, the application of the microscope to the study of the human organism, is an aspect of science not so far represented in the Académie. I am not worried about his philosophical beliefs except for the harm they may do to his work; in the case of a scientist, a man who must always be at grips with the experimental method, I am much afraid that any pretensions to philosophy may simply mean that he is a man with a system, a man of preconceived, unalterable ideas. Moreover, I must admit quite frankly that I do not feel at all competent to hold any opinion about contemporary philosophical trends. In the writings of M. Comte, I have read only a few ridiculous passages; and in those of M. Littré, only the fine few pages inspired by his outstanding scholarship and some of his domestic virtues. My own philosophy is entirely of the heart, not the mind; I yield, for instance, to those feelings which are eternal in so natural a way, and which a man feels at the bedside of a child whom he has cherished and who has just departed from this life. At that transcendent moment, something in the depths of a man's soul says the world may well be more than a set of phenomena tending to a mechanical equilibrium, phenomena which have

* In answer to a letter from Sainte-Beuve asking Pasteur to vote for the anatomist, Charles Robin, a candidate for membership of the Académie des Sciences.

simply emerged from chaos through the gradual operation of material forces.

Our great philosophers . . . I admire them all! As for people like myself, men whose ideas are always being corrected and modified by experiment, we are continually made to see that nature—if I may put it like this—is different, even in the least of her manifestations, from what we thought she was. And the philosophers, guessing away—stuck behind that dense curtain, the problem of the beginning and the end of all things—how on earth do they ever acquire any knowledge about anything?

But forgive me for running on like this. Let me return to the subject of your delightful letter, so full of the arts of persuasion. What draws me strongly to M. Robin is that he is better known that his competitor, and that I have been told he enjoys the patronage of a colleague for whom I have an equal admiration and affection, M. Claude Bernard. I will say nothing of a certain other patronage which you mischievously indicate in your letter, because my philosophy, *which is of the heart, not the head*,* might let me down.

Meanwhile I owe it to M. Lacaze-du-Tiers, who was a colleague of mine at Lille, a man of real merit whose appointment I requested at the École Normale as successor to M. Valenciennes, to wait until I can discuss with him Robin's research-work and claims to reputation.

Believe me, etc.,†
L. PASTEUR.

TO A SICK CHILD

My dear little Gueyton, why haven't you kept your word and sent me your news? I am afraid the reason may be that you don't know how to write. If that's the case, do everything you can to learn to read and write well. If you need money so as to be able to take some time off and pay a teacher, let me know. Your face, and the good character which stands written there,

---

* *Qui est toute de sentiment*; underlined by Pasteur. The mysterious patronage to which he alludes was that of the Princesse Mathilde.

† *Veuillez agréer, Monsieur et cher Maître et très illustre confrère, l'hommage de mon profond respect et de mon dévouement.* (*Tr.*)

have given me a keen interest in your welfare. I am sure that you can easily learn, and that you'll be able to get a suitable job in consequence. Now tell me about your family. Have you a father and mother? Have you any brothers and sisters? If you can't write, get the mayor of your commune, or the school-master, or the priest, to send me your answers. Get well quickly. Goodbye for now.

I am enclosing a postal order for ten francs.

A REPORT ON FERMENTATIONS
ADDRESSED TO THE MINISTER OF EDUCATION*

"Plants take from the air about them, from water and in general from the mineral realm, the materials they need for their growth.

"Animals feed either on plants or on other animals which feed on plants, with the result that the materials of which animals are constituted are taken, in the ultimate analysis, from the air and the mineral realm.

"Finally, fermentation, putrefaction and combustion are continually returning to the atmosphere and the mineral realm the principles which plants and animals have taken from them. By what means does nature maintain this wonderful circulation between the three realms?"

These words, sir, quoted from a posthumous paper which a reverent hand has found among the manuscripts of Lavoisier, present with admirable clarity the three terms of the great problem of the perpetuity of life on the surface of the earth. The first two comprise the whole field of modern physiology; the third—namely that described by Lavoisier as the perpetual return to the air and the mineral realm of the principles which plants and animals have borrowed from them—is a field of study the exploration of which has as yet hardly begun.

It almost puts me out of countenance to have to tell you that this is the field I have dared to make my own. At any rate, this is the field which I have long striven to illuminate by direct

---

* This letter, taken from the *Correspondance de Pasteur*, is dated simply April, 1862; the day of the month is not given.

experiment and on which I have in fact been lucky enough to shed a little light, as I shall endeavour to show in a moment. First, however, I want to give you some idea of the interest of my investigations.

We know that substances extracted from plants ferment if left to themselves, and that they gradually disappear through contact with the air. We also know that the dead bodies of animals putrefy, and that within a short time only their skeletons remain. Such destruction of dead organic matter is one of the conditions for the perpetuation of life. If the withered remains of dead plants, and the corpses of animals, were not destroyed, the earth's surface would be encumbered with organic matter and life would become impossible, because the cycle of transformation indicated by Lavoisier would be incomplete. In other words, when in any living creature the internal processes regulated by the laws of life have ceased to operate, the work of death has only just begun. That work is not ended until the organic matter of the dead creature, be it animal or plant, has returned to the primal simplicity of mineral substances and reactions.

The fibrin of our muscles, the albumen of our blood, the gelatine of our bones, the urea in our urine, the lignous matter in plants, the sugar of their fruit, the starch of their seeds, etc.— all these have to be reduced little by little to water, ammonia and carbonic acid, so that the elementary principles of those complex organic materials can be taken up again by plants and re-combined to form the food of new organisms of the kinds which gave them birth, and so on perpetually, from age to age.

How are these transformations effected? That is the problem; it is subdivided into a multitude of other problems which are full of interest and promise, and which I am rash enough to be trying to solve. I have devoted six years of unremitting work to them, and I think I can confidently say that my preliminary results appear to afford even now a glimpse of the highest, most general law governing this order of phenomena. The conclusion I have reached is this: the destruction of organic materials is chiefly due to the multiplication of microscopic living creatures endowed with special properties for the dissociation of complex organic materials or for slow combustion and the fixation of oxygen; properties which make these microscopic creatures the most active agents of that indispensable reaction to which I referred above—the return to the atmosphere of everything which once had life.

I have proved that the atmosphere in which we live swarms with the germs of these microscopic creatures, which are always ready to multiply in dead matter wherever it presents itself, and thus to fulfil the mission of destruction which is correlative to their life. And if God had not so arranged things that, under normal conditions of life and health, the laws governing the changes in the tissues and fluids of animals' bodies did not impede the proliferation of these microscopic creatures, we should always be vulnerable to their inroads. But the moment the breath of life is extinguished there is no part of any plant or animal organism which does not become their food. In short, life reappears in a new form after death, and with new properties. The ubiquitous germs of microscopic organisms then begin their development; it is their influence which, in one context, causes organic matter to gasify by fermentation, and, in another, makes atmospheric oxygen combine with it in large quantities and slowly brings about its complete combustion.

You will have begun to see how vast and also how useful is this field of studies, which presents so many connections with various diseases of animals and plants, and which has undoubtedly enabled us to make the first steps towards effective research into putrid and infectious diseases. But allow me, sir, to abandon general considerations and enable you as it were to put your finger on one of the many phenomena governed by the universal law of the death and destruction of all living creatures.

Let us picture to ourselves, if we can, the enormous quantity of sugary substances which nature accumulates every year in the plants growing on the surface of the globe. It is an absolute necessity that these billions of pounds of sugar be destroyed and returned to the air of the atmosphere. If man, who uses some of this sugar for his own nutrition, were to burn none of it by the act of respiration, the incalculable masses of sugar would nevertheless undergo complete combustion. For, I repeat, it is part of the laws of the permanence of life on the Earth's surface that everything forming part of a plant or an animal should be destroyed and transformed into mineral, gaseous, volatile substances.

What then are the means employed by nature for destroying the prodigious masses of sugary material produced yearly by the plant kingdom? Whenever any quantity of a sugary juice is left to its own devices, the air contributes to it the germ of a minute mycodermic plant which propagates itself in the juice with remarkable ease, and, concomitantly with the life and growth of this plant, the sugar is transformed into alcohol and carbonic acid gas.

This tiny plant is one of the numerous organic ferments of sugar. We see that in this, the first phase of the process, part of the sugar has already been returned to the atmosphere, since one of the substances given off in its decomposition is carbonic acid gas.

But the alcohol still remains to be destroyed.

Now I have recently established, with complete certainty, that the alcohol is destroyed through the agency of a microscopic plant which differs from the previous one, but whose germ is similarly conveyed by the air to the new, alcoholic liquor; and that this plant possesses the very remarkable property of combining atmospheric oxygen with the alcohol and thus converting the latter into acetic acid. Next, if the action of this microscopic plant is allowed to continue, the oxidation of which it is the necessary agent affects the acetic acid itself and transforms the whole of it into carbonic acid gas and water; these two substances are the final terms in the destruction of sugar and its complex return to the air of the atmosphere. Microscopic organisms are the hidden agents of this natural phenomenon, by virtue of the admirable properties with which the Almighty has endowed them.

I need not add that by arresting the combustion of sugar at

the stage of alcohol, and that of alcohol at the stage of acetic acid, man's industry has created wine, beer and vinegar. . . .

And does not this, sir, make it clear that the highest activities of pure science cannot advance a single step without sooner or later contributing to the industrial applications of science? It was in fact while studying the above series of phenomena, with the sole intention of discovering their initial cause and the factors governing that cause, that I discovered two new principles which are present in all fermented liquors: succinic acid and glycerine, which are contained in wine, for example, in the high proportion of 8 or 9 grammes per litre.

This fact had not previously been so much as suspected. And I might mention in passing, as an additional pointer to the fruitfulness of pure science from the practical point of view, that this was the reason why the artificial manufacture of wine was impossible at the period of the vine disease, when it is said that the Emperor, in his enlightened solicitude, suggested that the shortage of natural wine be remedied by the manufacture of an artificial wine containing the same principles.

It would certainly have been possible, in response to the Emperor's wish, to manufacture a drink with some resemblance to wine; but it would inevitably have been without seven or eight grammes of glycerine per litre, since no one knew that the natural product contained glycerine. And since this substance is an essential component of all oily substances, it may be presumed that the artificial wine would have lacked one of its most beneficial ingredients.

Finally, to end this sketch of the services which pure science, without express intention and merely as a by-product of its activities, can render to practical manufacture, my recent discovery, which I have just communicated to the Academy, of the microscopic vegetable ferment which converts alcohol into acetic acid will enable me to indicate a new process, of great simplicity, for the manufacture of that acid; an advance of which industry will doubtless make profitable use.

If, sir, I were to enlarge further on the results I have already achieved, I would be afraid of abusing your indulgence.

F

Nevertheless there is one more result, a strange one, about which I should like to tell you. I have discovered an infusorial animalcule which is one of the principal agents of putrefaction and which possesses the singular faculty, previously unknown to the natural sciences, of living without air: indeed, it dies on being brought into contact with air, and simultaneously loses its wonderful power of putrefaction. But I must rest content with this endeavour to convey the goal towards which all my present research is directed. What I am doing is to study, with the aid of rigorous experimentation, the physiological role (which I believe to be immense) of the infinitely small in the general economy of nature.

As the Académie des Sciences awarded to my initial studies of this subject two of the major prizes at its disposition, namely the Prix de Physiologie Expérimentale, in 1859, and the Prix Jecker, in 1861, I have the honour of enclosing herewith the reports made in connection with these prizes by MM. Claude Bernard and Chevreul. These testimonials from the leading scientific body in Europe will be an assurance to Your Excellency both of the good use to which your liberality is being put, and of my continued effort to fulfil, in so far as it lies within my power, the wishes expressed to you by the Emperor, and to satisfy the unexpected interest which His Majesty has been so kind as to take in my work.

I remain, with profound respect,

Your Excellency's most humble servant.

On the Nature of Fermentations

In the various communications which I have had the honour
of addressing to the Academy on the subject of fermentations
properly so called, although all my efforts were directed towards demonstrating that fermentations were correlative to
the presence and proliferation of living organisms, with a
different organism corresponding to each type of fermentation,
I abstained from expressing any opinion as to the cause of these
mysterious phenomena. The purpose of my inquiries has been
to study the products of fermentations more closely than had
been done before, to isolate the ferments, and to discover
experimental proofs of their structure and mode of life. As
regards the leading idea, that of the organic nature of ferments,
any possible doubts which may have remained in a few people's
minds must have been removed by the results which I recently
had the honour of presenting before the Academy, on the
subject of butyric fermentation.

I declared in effect that the butyric ferment was an infusorial
animalcule, or, if we wish to avoid prejudicing the question of
the frontier between the two organic realms, that the butyric
ferment was an organism, moving and producing in the same
way as the organisms known to naturalists as vibrios. But what
I am now in a position to remark is that the butyric ferment
carries in itself, in its movements and its mode of generation,
the evident proof of its organic character.

There are, then, other organic ferments besides brewer's
yeast. Despite the opposition encountered at first by this idea,
I make bold to hope that it can be regarded today as an
addition to scientific knowledge.

A no less important question now presents itself: how do living organisms perform their role in fermentation?

As I have mentioned, the butyric ferment is a living organism resembling a vibrio. If, as I have done by direct experimentation, we study the mode of life of the vibrios so far described by naturalists, we see that they extract considerable quantities of oxygen from the atmospheric air, and that they give off carbonic acid. My experiments show that exactly the same can be said of the mucidineae, the torulaceae, and the mucors.* Like infusoria, these minute plants cannot do without oxygen. Furthermore, and again like ordinary infusoria, these plants do not possess the character of ferments: that is to say that the chemical phenomena which they cause in their food-materials are of the order of the phenomena of nutrition, in which the weight of food-material assimilated corresponds to the weight of tissue transformed by means of it.

Things are far otherwise with the vibrio of butyric fermentation, concerning which I have observed two facts: first, that it lives without free oxygen, and second, that it is a ferment.

It matters little whether the advance of science, determining the frontier between the two realms, shows this vibrio to be a plant or an animal: since to live without air and to be a ferment are two properties which distinguish it from all the lower species of both realms. This point must be clearly grasped.

Taking the facts together, we are led to wonder whether there may not be a hidden relationship between the property of being a ferment and that of living without atmospheric air, since we observe the ferment-property in the butyric vibrio, which lives without oxygen, whereas the same property is not possessed by ordinary vibrios and moulds, in which life without oxygen is impossible.

The foregoing is a faithful account of the chain of facts suggested to me by the new experiments and views which I shall now proceed to describe.

In a balloon-shaped retort with a capacity of a quarter of a litre I place about 100 cubic centimetres of sugared water

* In other words, broadly speaking, moulds or lower fungi.

mixed with albuminoid substances. The neck of the retort is then drawn out over a flame, and the exiguous open end is placed in a bath of mercury. The liquid in the retort is brought to the boil so as to drive out both the air in the retort and that dissolved in the liquid. During cooling, mercury enters the retort. Next, after breaking the tapered part of the neck by knocking it against the bottom of the mercury bath, I introduce a very small quantity of brewer's yeast into the retort without allowing any air to enter at the same time.

The experiment shows that the yeast globules increase in number, though sluggishly, and that the sugar ferments.

In these conditions, 1 part of yeast (by weight) will decompose 60, or 80, or 100 parts of sugar. The conclusion is that brewer's yeast is capable of multiplying in the complete absence of free oxygen, and that it then displays in a high degree the property of a ferment.

This much being established, let us repeat the experiment; but this time we shall allow the presence of plenty of free air, as a source of oxygen. For this purpose I take a broad, shallow glass dish and place in it a thin layer of sugared water with albuminoids and sow a small quantity of yeast in this medium, the dish being more or less uncovered and freely exposed to the atmosphere.

In the event of our wishing to analyse the gases and study the alteration of the air, we must use a large flask with a flat bottom and close its neck with the flame, tapering it at the same time, so that it will be easy to break off the tip later under the surface of a mercury bath, with a view to collecting the escaping gases and determining the ratio of the volumes of oxygen and nitrogen.

In experiments conducted in this manner we find that the yeast multiplies remarkably, with a vigour not previously observed in this little plant. The experiment with the large flask proves, moreover, that the yeast globules extract a considerable quantity of oxygen from the air. There is no comparison between the speed of development of the yeast cells in these conditions and in the circumstances examined in the first place, when there was no free oxygen. It would be no exaggeration to say that they multiply a hundred times faster in the one case than in the other.

It follows from these experiments that brewer's yeast has two distinct modes of existence. Free oxygen may be entirely absent, or it may be present in any volume. In the latter event it is taken up and used by the plant, whose vital processes are extraordinarily enhanced; and it then lives like the lower plants in general. And just as I had previously observed that, as regards the assimiliation of carbon, phosphates, and nitrogen, brewer's yeast was essentially similar to the mucidineae, so now it is equally certain that if yeast is allowed to breathe free oxygen its mode of life is comparable to that of the lower plants and animalculae. But experimentation shows that the analogy goes further still and extends to the fermentation property. For if we measure the fermenting power of yeast when it is allowed to assimilate free oxygen, we find that this power has almost completely disappeared.

. . . These are the bare facts. Now, what is their immediate consequence? Are we forced to conclude that yeast, so greedy for oxygen that it busily absorbs it from the air of the atmosphere, can be denied free oxygen and show no need of it, provided that plenty of oxygen is presented to it in the form of a chemical compound in the fermentescible medium?

In this lies the whole mystery of fermentation! For if the question I have asked be answered by saying, "Since brewer's yeast absorbs oxygen plentifully when the gas is present in the free state, the reason must be that it needs oxygen in order to live, so that it has to take oxygen from the fermentescible medium when no free oxygen is present"—the plant is immediately revealed to be an agent of the decomposition of sugar: at every respiratory movement on the part of its cells, there will be molecules of sugar whose equilibrium is destroyed by subtraction of part of their oxygen. A phenomenon of decomposition will be the result and the plant assumes the character of a ferment; a character which it lacks whenever there is free oxygen available for it to consume.

To sum up, alongside all previously known organisms, organisms which without exception (or so it is believed) can breathe and feed only by absorbing free oxygen, there exists another class of organisms, whose respiration is sufficiently active for them to be able to live in an airless environment, by extracting oxygen from certain compounds; with the result that the latter are slowly and progressively decomposed.

This second category of organisms would consist of the ferments, similar in every way to the members of the first category, living as those do—assimilating carbon, nitrogen and phosphates, and requiring oxygen—but differing from them by possessing the property of breathing oxygen extracted from relatively unstable compounds, in the absence of free oxygen.

Such are the facts, and the theory that seems to be their natural expression, which I have the honour of submitting to the judgement of the Academy; and of which I hope to add new experimental proofs in the near future.

(Note to the Académie des Sciences, June 17, 1861, entitled *Expériences et vues nouvelles sur la nature des fermentations*.)

On Antiseptic Methods*

IF I had the honour of being a surgeon, I would never introduce any instrument whatsoever into the human body without having first passed it through boiling water and, more efficaciously still, through a naked flame, and then rapidly cooling it.

... The water and sponge and lint with which you wash and dress a wound leave germs in it, which, as you see, multiply with great ease and rapidity in the tissues and would certainly cause the death of every surgical patient were it not that life, in the patient's system, fights the multiplication of the germs.†

But alas! how often does not this vital resistance prove ineffective! How often do not the patient's constitution, his physical weakness, his state of mind, and the faulty dressings, offer an inadequate barrier to the invasion of the "infinitely small" with which you have unwittingly covered the affected part!

If I had the honour of being a surgeon, convinced as I am of the dangers to which we are exposed by the microbial germs on the surfaces of all the objects about us, especially in hospitals, not only would I use absolutely clean instruments but, after washing my hands with the greatest care and submitting them to momentary contact with a flame (with no more discomfort than a smoker feels when passing a glowing coal rapidly from one hand to the other), I would use no lint, bandages or sponges

* This extract consists of two passages from notes to the Académie des Sciences: the first paragraph is dated January 5, 1874; the remainder, April 29, 1878. Both notes will be found in their entirety in the *Œuvres complètes de Pasteur*, Vol. VI, published by Masson, Paris.

† A noteworthy foreshadowing of antibodies and other defences possessed by the organism.

which had not been exposed to air at a temperature of 130°
to 150°. All the water I used would previously have been
raised for some time to 110° or 120°. All these precautions are
thoroughly practicable.

I should thus have to fear only the germs floating in the air
round the patient's bed, but observation tells us every day that
the number of such germs is practically insignificant compared
with those in the dust on the surfaces of objects, and in the most
limpid water-supplies. And there would be nothing to prevent
me from using antiseptic methods of wound-dressing as well,
but if adopted in conjunction with the precautions I have indicated, these methods could be very greatly simplified. Dilute
carbolic acid, non-caustic and hence innocuous to the hands
and respiratory passages of the operator, could be advantage-
ously substituted for caustic carbolic acid.*

---

* Used during operations by surgeons, following Lister's example, for
sprinkling their hands and the affected area of the patient's body.

Developing the Antirabic Vaccine

As a result of many experiments, so many as to be almost past counting, I have arrived at a quick, practical, prophylactic method whose successes in the case of dogs have been so numerous and so consistent that I feel confident it can be applied to animals in general, and even to human beings.

The method is essentially based on the following facts:

If, after trepanning, the dura mater of a rabbit is inoculated with spinal cord taken from a stray dog with rabies, the rabbit invariably develops the disease, after an average incubation-period of approximately a fortnight.

If virus from this rabbit is transferred to a second, and from the latter to a third, and so on successively, by the same method of inoculation, the incubation-period shows a tendency to become shorter, and this tendency becomes progressively more marked as the series continues.

By the time some twenty to twenty-five transfers from rabbit to rabbit have been completed, incubation may be as little as eight days, and this figure remains steady during the next twenty to twenty-five transfers. It then falls to seven days and remains there with remarkable consistency until the total number of transfers reaches ninety. That is as far as I have got at the moment, and the present incubation period is very slightly under seven days.

These experiments were begun in 1882 and have now been going on for three years in unbroken succession, without my having had to obtain a fresh supply of virus from an outside source; each rabbit has been inoculated from the dead body of its predecessor. It is thus a simple matter to have constantly available, over a considerable period of time, a rabic virus of perfect purity, always identical in its characteristics or nearly so. This is the crux of the *practical* side of the method.

The spinal cord of these rabbits is consistently virulent, and the virulence is equally strong throughout the length of the cord.

If we cut off portions of cord a few centimetres long, taking every care not to let them get contaminated, and hang them in dry air, the virulence gradually diminishes and finally ceases altogether. The time taken for the virulence to die out varies slightly with the thickness of the cord, but depends chiefly on the temperature of the air. The lower the temperature the longer the virulence lasts. These facts are the crux of the *scientific* side of the method.

On this basis, the following is the method for rendering a dog immune to rabies within a comparatively short time.

In a series of flasks, the air in which is kept dry by pieces of potash lying on the bottom of each flask, we hang each day a piece of fresh virulent cord from a rabbit which has died of rabies; the incubation period having been seven days.

Each day, the dog is inoculated under the skin with a full Pravaz syringe of sterilised *bouillon* in which we have dissolved a small piece of one of the cords undergoing desiccation, beginning with a cord some distance away in the series from the date of the day of the injection; previous experiments have indicated the right interval.

On the succeeding days the same procedure is carried out with fresher portions of cord at two-day intervals, until the highly virulent last cord is reached, which has been in its flask for only a day or two.

The dog is now resistant to rabies. It can be inoculated with rabic virus subcutaneously, or even on the surface of the brain (by trepanning), but will not develop the disease.

By applying this method, I had obtained fifty dogs of different breeds and ages, all resistant to rabies, and had not a single failure, when, suddenly, on Monday, the 6th of last July, three people from Alsace arrived at my laboratory: Théodore Vone, a grocer from Meissengott, near Sélestat, whose dog had developed rabies and bitten him on the arm on July 4; Joseph Meister, aged nine, who had also been bitten on July 4, at eight in the morning, by the same dog; and the little boy's mother, who had not been bitten.

Joseph Meister had numerous bites—on his hands, legs and thighs; some of them were deep and made it difficult for him to walk. The worst of these bites had been cauterised with carbolic acid by Dr. Weber, of Villé, but not until eight o'clock in the evening on July 4, twelve hours after the accident.

The dog had been destroyed by its master. When the body was opened the stomach was found to be full of hay, straw and fragments of wood. The dog was undoubtedly rabid. Joseph Meister, when pulled from underneath it, had been covered with blood and slobber.

M. Vone displayed marked contusions on his arms, but assured me that the dog's teeth had not penetrated through his shirt. As he had nothing to fear, I told him he could return to Alsace the same day, which he did, but I kept back little Meister and his mother.

The weekly session of the Académie des Sciences was due for that very day, July 6; I attended it, and saw our colleague Dr. Vulpian, to whom I described what had happened. Dr. Vulpian, and Professor Grancher of the Faculty of Medicine, were kind enough to come and see little Joseph Meister at once and observe the number and nature of his wounds, of which there were no less than fourteen.

The opinion of our learned colleague and Dr. Grancher was that in view of the number and gravity of the bites Joseph Meister was almost certain to contract rabies. I then told M. Vulpian and M. Grancher about the new results I had achieved in the study of rabies since reading my paper on it in Copenhagen last year.

The child's death appeared inevitable. I decided, not without acute and harrowing anxiety, as may be imagined, to apply to Joseph Meister the method which I had found consistently successful with dogs.

It was true that my fifty dogs had not been bitten before I had rendered them resistant to rabies, but I knew this fact could be dismissed from my calculations because I had obtained resistance to rabies in a large number of other dogs after they had been bitten. I had demonstrated this new and important piece of progress to the members of the Rabies Commission earlier this year.

So at 8 p.m. on July 6, sixty hours after the infliction of the bites on July 4, treatment was begun in the presence of Drs. Vulpian and Grancher: half a Pravaz syringeful of the spinal cord of a rabbit which had died of rabies on June 21, the cord having been kept in dry air since that time, that is to say for a fortnight, was injected in a fold of the young patient's skin, in the region of his right hip.

During the succeeding days new inoculations were given, in the same region, though not all on the same side; the time table was as follows:

Half a Pravaz Syringe

7 July,   9 a.m., spinal cord of 23 June, 14 days old.
7 July,   6 a.m., spinal cord of 25 June, 12 days old.
8 July,   9 a.m., spinal cord of 27 June, 11 days old.
8 July, 11 a.m., spinal cord of 29 June, 9 days old.
9 July, 11 a.m., spinal cord of 1 July, 8 days old.
10 July, 11 a.m., spinal cord of 3 July, 7 days old.
11 July, 11 a.m., spinal cord of 5 July, 6 days old.
12 July, 11 a.m., spinal cord of 7 July, 5 days old.
13 July, 11 a.m., spinal cord of 9 July, 4 days old.
14 July, 11 a.m., spinal cord of 11 July, 3 days old.
15 July, 11 a.m., spinal cord of 13 July, 2 days old.
16 July, 11 a.m., spinal cord of 15 July, 1 day old.

Thus, I had thirteen inoculations given in all, over a period of ten days. I shall explain later that a smaller number of inoculations would have sufficed, but it will readily be understood that, in this first trial, I had to proceed with more than ordinary circumspection.

Each spinal cord used was also used for inoculating, by means of trepanning, two uninfected rabbits, so that the degree of virulence of all the cords could be checked. Observation of these animals showed that the cords of July 6, 7, 8, 9 and 10 were non-virulent, since none of the rabbits developed rabies. All the cords of July 11, 12, 13, 14, 15 and 16 were virulent, and the degree of virulence was progressively greater. Rabies declared itself after seven days in the rabbits inoculated on July 15 and 16; after eight days in those inoculated on July 12 and 14; and after fifteen days in those inoculated on July 11.

This means that in the closing days of the treatment I had inoculated Joseph Meister with the most virulent rabic virus obtainable, that of a dog reinforced by being passed through a long succession of rabbits; a virus which gives rabies to a rabbit after seven days of incubation, and to a dog after ten days. My justification for doing this was my experience with the fifty dogs mentioned above.

Once immunity had been attained the most virulent virus, in any quantity, can be injected without ill effects. My impression has always been that this merely has the effect of consolidating the immunity.

Joseph Meister has therefore escaped, not only the rabies which might have developed from his bites, but also that with which I inoculated him in order to test the immunity conferred by the treatment; a rabies more virulent than that of a stray dog.

The final, intensely virulent inoculation has the further advantage of limiting the period during which anxiety is felt about the consequences of the bite or bites. If it was possible for rabies to develop, it would do so more quickly as a result of a virus more virulent than that communicated by the bites. From the middle of August onward, I felt confident about the future of little Meister's health. Today, three months and three weeks after the accident, his health still leaves nothing to be desired.

(From Pasteur's communication to the Académie des Sciences, October 26, 1885; Œuvres complètes, Masson, Paris, Vol. VI.)

Pasteur as a Senatorial Candidate*

My dear compatriot,—Having been urgently invited to stand as a candidate in the election of a Senator to represent our *département*, I have gratefully accepted; and I now ask for your support.

I am not a politician at all.

I have no connection with any party.

I have never concerned myself with politics, so there is much I do not know. But one thing which I do know, and which is very much to the point, is this: I love my country and have served it with all my might. That is my profession of faith.

Another pertinent fact, which I have learnt by observation, is that there is nothing more harmful than the spirit of systematic opposition, the spirit which tries to bring about improvements not by preservation but by destruction.

I shall never enter into any association which aims at overthrowing the established order of things. The constitution, and the powers of the illustrious Marshal and President, are the law of the land. That law commands my devotion; and I shall help our country, as it is the duty of every good citizen to do, to regain her greatness and prosperity in the serious trial which she is now making of the republican system.

Men should be judged by what they have done, rather than by what they promise to do in future when their self-interest is in command of their tongues. So I beg leave to lay before you three documents which will tell you what manner of man I am.

* This appeal, dated January 15, 1875, was unsuccessful; Pasteur received a mere sixty-four votes.

The first is a pamphlet I published in 1871, entitled *A Correspondence between a French Scientist and a Prussian Scientist during the War*.

The second is a speech which attracted a certain amount of attention, and which I delivered on August 8, 1874, at the prize-giving at the school at Arbois. From it you will gather in what spirit of independence I shall defend science and the true principles of science.

The third is a note on some of my researches, followed by the text of the law voted on July 18, 1874, under which a recompense from the nation was awarded to me for those researches.

I am confident that this latter point will attract your attention, and that, on the solemn occasion with which you are now faced, you will demand the honour of commemorating an event which redounds to the glory of the *département* of the Jura.

You will not have forgotten that I was nominated a Senator on July 27, 1870, "for services rendered to science", that that nomination was never put into effect, and that it was so completely non-political in character that the Republic has since rewarded the services in question in an equally unusual way. . . .

It is therefore science in all its purity, dignity and independence which I shall be representing if you honour me with your vote.

Chronological Outline of Pasteur's Life

1822   December 27th, Pasteur born at Dôle (Jura).

1827   The Pasteur family settles at Arbois.

1838   In October Pasteur goes to Paris to become a pupil at the Pension Barbet; returns to Arbois in November. Takes drawing lessons.

1839   Begins his secondary education by becoming a boarder at the Collège Royal, Besançon.

1842   Is accepted by the École Normale, but being dissatisfied with his results (sixteenth out of twenty-three) does not take up his place.

1843   Second journey to Paris, to complete his secondary education (Pension Barbet, Lycée Saint-Louis, Sorbonne). Accepted again by the École Normale (position fifth this time).

1844   At the École Normale, begins study of chemistry and crystallography.

1845   Working for two degrees: the *licence ès sciences* and the *agrégation de physique*.

1846   Obtains his *agrégation*. Becomes an assistant teacher of chemistry at the École Normale (setting up the experiments required by the professor for teaching purposes). Research under Balard.

1847   Completes his chemistry thesis and physics thesis.

1848   First note to the Académie des Sciences, on dimorphism. Is appointed physics teacher at the Lycée at Dijon. Monograph on his first great discovery, the separation of paratartaric acid into its two opposite optical components. Death of his mother at Arbois.

1849   Is appointed professor at the Académie des Sciences de Strasbourg. Research in crystallography; several papers written. Marriage to Marie Laurent, daughter of the Dean of the Faculty.

1850   Research on the relationship between chemical composition, crystalline form and optical properties (rotation of plane of polarised light). Birth of his daughter, Jeanne. Death of his sister, Joséphine.

1851   Continues his research on molecular dissymmetry. Asserts that for every atomic group there is a possible inverse form (that, e.g., in the case of any dextro-rotatory substance it is possible to discover the corresponding laevo-rotatory form of the same substance). Birth of his second child, a son, Jean-Baptiste.

1852   Travels in Germany, Austria and Italy, in search of racemic (paratartaric) acid.

1853   Transformation of tartaric acid into racemic acid. Is nominated *Chevalier de la Légion d'Honneur*. Attempts to investigate "cosmic dissymmetry" with instruments of his own invention. Birth of his third child, a daughter, Cécile.

1854   Is appointed Professor of Chemistry at the new Faculty of Science at Lille; is also appointed Dean of the Faculty.

1855   Begins studying fermentation.

1856   Is a candidate for membership of the Académie des Sciences (Mineralogical Section).

1857   Fails to be elected to Académie des Sciences. Publishes a paper on lactic fermentation. Rumford Medal awarded by the Royal Society, London. Is appointed Administrator and Director of Scientific Studies at the École Normale.

1858   Research on alcoholic fermentation. Sets up a laboratory in an attic at the École Normale. Birth of his fourth child, a daughter, Marie-Louise.

1859   Publishes a paper on alcoholic fermentation. Begins research on spontaneous generation. Wins prize for experimental physiology, offered by the Académie des Sciences. Death of his eldest daughter, Jeanne.

1860   Experiments on spontaneous generation. Serious material difficulties caused by lack of equipment for his laboratory.

1861   Discovers anaerobiosis. Is awarded the Prix Jecker of the Académie des Sciences for his research on fermentation.

1862   Is elected to the Mineralogical Section of the Académie des Sciences. Papers on vinegar. Exposition of the part played by the "infinitely small" in nature. Wins Prix Alhumbert for research on spontaneous generation. Death of Biot.

1863   Papers on wine. Controversy with Pouchet on spontaneous generation. Is appointed Professor of Geology, Physics and Chemistry at the École des Beaux Arts. Birth of his fifth child, a daughter, Camille.

1864   Publishes a paper on acetic fermentation. Violent controversies with Pouchet, Joly and Musset on spontaneous generation. Sets up a laboratory at Arbois for research on wine.

1865   Work on pasteurisation (improving the keeping qualities of wine by heating). Begins studying diseases of silkworms. Makes a stay at the imperial palace at Compiègne. Death of his father at Arbois. Death of his daughter, Camille.

1866   Long stay in the South of France (study of silkworm diseases). Publishes an essay on the work of Claude Bernard. Publication of *Études sur le vin*. Dispute about priority in the application of heat to wine to make it keep. Death of his daughter, Cécile.

1867   Grand Prix of the Universal Exhibition, for pasteurisation. More work on silkworm diseases (investigation of *flacherie* as well as *pébrine*, the disease he had originally been asked to study). The "École Normale incident"; Pasteur shows himself a rigid disciplinarian. Resigns his appointment at the École Normale (but keeps his laboratory there, and continues work in it for the rest of his life). Is appointed Professor of Chemistry at the Sorbonne.

1868   Publication of *Études sur le vinaigre*. Laboratory at the École Normale is enlarged. Pasteur is promoted to be *Commandeur de la Légion d'Honneur*. Attack of paralysis, ending in permanent hemiplegia (but intellectual faculties unimpaired).

1869   New research on silkworm diseases; in connection with this, Pasteur makes a stay on the estate of the Prince Imperial at Vicentina, in Austria. Violent controversies with his detractors.

1870   Publication of *Études sur la maladie des vers à soie*. Pasteur makes a declaration of exacerbated patriotism.

1871   As a protest against "Prussian barbarism", Pasteur informs the University of Bonn that he is relinquishing the degree of doctor of medicine, *honoris causa*, awarded to him by that University in 1868. He takes up a conservative attitude to the Commune. Stays at Clermont-Ferrand; begins research on beer, and travels to London in connection with it.

1872   Hotly contested arguments with Frémy, at the Académie des Sciences, on the origin of ferments. Restatement of his claims to priority in heat-treatment of wine.

1873   Official recommendation is made that the State award Pasteur a "national recompense". Pasteur is elected to the Académie de Médecine.

1874   Lister applies antisepsis to surgery, and says the method originated in Pasteur's work. "National recompense" (a permanent income) officially voted.

1875   A new laboratory is set up at Arbois for the study of fermentations. Publication of *Études sur la bière*.

1876   Pasteur a candidate for the Senate; bases his electoral campaign on the need for adequate subsidies to French science; exalts the role of scientists in society, but in general takes up a conservative attitude; is not elected. Refutation of Bastian's experiments.

1877   Begins research on anthrax; also on septicaemia and puerperal fever. Sharp controversy with Bastian on spontaneous generation. Discovers the septic vibrio.

1878   Journey to Italy. Refutation of a posthumous paper of Claude Bernard on fermentation. Violent dispute with Berthelot, who had unearthed this paper. Controversies with several people, especially Colin, on the aetiology of anthrax. Research on gangrene. Publication of a paper on *La théorie des germes et ses applications à la médecine et à la chirurgie*.

1879   Research on chicken cholera. Discovery of how to confer immunisation by using attenuated cultures. Pasteur's daughter, Marie-Louise, marries René Vallery-Radot (later the brilliant biographer of Pasteur). Discovery of streptococcus.

1880   Pasteur begins his research on rabies. His work is violently attacked at the Académie de Médecine, and he thinks of resigning his membership. Guérin challenges him to a duel. Publication of a paper, *Sur les maladies virulentes et en particulier sur la maladie appelée vulgairement choléra des poules*. Death of his sister, Virginie. Discovery of staphylococcus and pneumococcus (which Pasteur at first mistook for the rabies virus).

1881   Publication of his studies on anthrax vaccination. Triumphant experiment on anthrax vaccination at Pouilly-le-Fort, near Melun. Communication to the International Medical Congress held in London. Pasteur is elected to the Académie Française. Research on yellow fever at Bordeaux.

1882   Renan pronounces Pasteur's *discours de réception* at the Académie Française, where Pasteur occupies the chair rendered vacant by the death of Littré. Anthrax vaccination begun in France and abroad. Research on pleuro-pneumonia in cattle. Communication to the Congress of Hygiene, at Geneva, on the attenuation of viruses. Controversy with Robert Koch on immunisation against anthrax. Work on swine erysipelas.

1883   Installation of a laboratory in the family house at Arbois. Controversy with the Veterinary Academy of Turin about anthrax vaccination. Outbreak of cholera in Egypt; to study the disease, a mission is sent, composed of Straus, Nocard, Roux and Thuillier; the last-named dies of cholera.

1884   Pasteur reads a paper to the International Medical Congress, Copenhagen, on microbes and vaccines. Research on rabies goes on. Difficulties of setting up kennels (for dogs to be used in experiments) at Ville-neuve-l'Étang.

1885   First antirabic vaccinations of human beings: Joseph Meister and J.-B. Jupille are successfully treated. Patients flock to Pasteur from all over France.

1886   Patients now arriving from all over world. Pasteur has never been held in higher veneration, and an international subscription is organised for the foundation of an "Institut Pasteur"; but attacks on him, at home and abroad, are also at their highest. Suffering from heart trouble, he goes for a holiday to Bordighera, but soon returns to Paris to battle with his contradictors.

1887   Plans made for the future Institut Pasteur. Attack by Dr. Peter, at the Académie de Médecine, on rabies prophylaxis; Pasteur is not there, but is defended by Dr. Grancher. Experiment on destroying rabbits (with which Australia is infested) by means of chicken cholera. Second paralytic attack (October 23).

1888   Loir is sent by Pasteur to Australia; encounters difficulties, has disagreement with Australian Government; nevertheless stays several years and does useful work. The Institut Pasteur is inaugurated.

1889   Pasteur feels that his strength is declining.

1892   Pasteur's jubilee at the Sorbonne, December 27.

1894   Pasteur makes his last stay at Arbois.

1895   Death of Pasteur at Villeneuve-l'Étang, September 28.

Glossary

ACID: Substances having a sharp sour taste (from the Latin, *acidus*, sour), e.g. vinegar is diluted acetic acid. Acids* form in solution a characteristic negatively charged acid radical.

ALCOHOLS: Neutral organic compounds containing a hydroxyl group (OH). Ethyl alcohol, spirits of wine, is the well-known product of alcoholic fermentation.

ALKALI or BASE: The opposites of acids, they give rise in solution (dissolving in water) to a characteristic positively charged basic radical. When added to an acid, they are said to neutralise the acid and the oppositely charged acidic and basic radicals combine to form a salt.

AMINES: Organic compounds containing Nitrogen, derived from, and having properties similar to, ammonia. The amines are generally weak bases and include the naturally occurring alkaloids, e.g. strychnine.

AMINO ACIDS: Organic compounds several of which are essential to the diet of humans and other living organisms. Sometimes referred to as "the fundamental bricks of life". They are bifunctional, containing both acidic and basic groups. Since each acid group can combine with the basic group in another amino acid, by repetition long chains are formed in which the individual amino acids form the links. These amino acid chains are the main constituent of the proteins.

---

* The above definitions of acids and bases were coined to assist the layman in the concept of salt-formation.

CARBOHYDRATES: Compounds of the general formula $(CH_2O_n$, of which glucose is the type. They are named according to the number of carbons, e.g. pentose or hexose. D-glucose, or dextrose, $C_6H_{12}O_6$, is the commonest hexose sugar; it is present in many plants, and is the sugar of the blood. Carbohydrates play an essential part in the metabolism of all organisms; they are the "fuel" of organic processes.

ESTERS: Fragrant compounds formed by condensing an acid with an alcohol. Ethyl alcohol with acetic acid forms ethyl acetate.

pH: A convenient measure of the acidity or basicity of an aqueous solution. The stronger the acidity of a solution, the smaller the pH value; the stronger the basicity, the larger the pH value. Neutral = pH 7; highly acid = pH O; highly basic (alkaline) = pH 14.

PHAGOCYTES: White corpuscles of blood (and lymph), which engulf particles from their surroundings by a process called phagocytosis. Phagocytes are highly mobile and devour not only fragments of tissue-debris but also any particles alien to the system, including pathogenic bacteria.

PROTEINS: Complex organic compounds which are important constituents of all living matter. They are made up of hundreds or even thousands of amino acids as well as other substances. Variation of the amino acids and the attached substances gives rise to numerous types of proteins.

RADICAL: A group of atoms which persist as a unit. This unit forms an integral part of a compound and may persist through a series of chemical processes. Thus the hydroxyl radical OH, is part of the water molecule H_2O, and also the alcohol molecule. The amino radical NH_2, is found in amines and amino acids.

REFRACTION: Change of direction undergone by electromagnetic waves on passing from one medium into another. Since white light consists of radiations of different wavelengths and the index of refraction is different for each wavelength, a prism separates the radiations into the components of the visible spectrum.

SALT: Substances resulting from the combination of an acid and a base. Common salt, sodium chloride, is obtained by the union of hydrochloric acid (spirits of salt) and soda. Perhaps the best known organic salt was prepared by Pasteur. He added cinchonicine (an alkaloid base) to paratartaric acid and separated the resultant salt, cinchonicine paratartrate, into two forms, one of which rotates the plane of polarised light to the left and the other to the right. This type of process, discovered by Pasteur, for separating optical isomers is an important technique of the modern laboratory.

Bibliography

ATTWOOD, EVELYN M., *Louis Pasteur* (Longmans, Green & Co., London, 1954).

COMPTON, PIERS, *The Genius of Louis Pasteur* (Grove Press, London and Manchester, 1939).

DESCOUR, L., *Pasteur and His Work*, Trans. A.F. & B. H. Wedd (T. Fisher Unwin, London, 1922).

DOORLY, ELEANOR, *The Microbe Man. A Life of Pasteur for Children* (Heffer, Cambridge, 1938).

DUBOS, R. J., *Louis Pasteur, Free Lance of Science* (Victor Gollancz, London, 1951).

DUCLAUX, ÉMILE, *Pasteur. The History of a Mind* (W. B. Saunders & Co., Philadelphia and London, 1920).

GRANT, MADELEINE P., *Louis Pasteur* (Ernest Benn, London, 1960).

HOLMES, SAMUEL J., *Louis Pasteur* (Chapman and Hall, London, 1925).

LEVY, JOSEPH H., *The Psychology of Pasteurism* (Lawrence Nelson, London, 1914).

NICOLLE, JACQUES, *Louis Pasteur. A Master of Scientific Enquiry* (Hutchinson, London, 1961).

PAGET, STEPHEN, *Pasteur and After Pasteur* (A. and C. Black, London, 1914).

PAIN, NESTA, *Louis Pasteur* (A. and C. Black, London, 1957).

VALLERY-RADOT, RENÉ, *Louis Pasteur, His Life and Labours*. Trans. Lady Claud Hamilton (Longmans, Green & Co., London, 1885).

Index